CROSS
WORDS
for
clever
Kids

Puzzles and solutions created by Gareth Moore

Illustrations by Chris Dickason

Edited by Bryony Jones

Cover design by Angie Allison

First published in Great Britain in 2015 by Buster Books,
an imprint of Michael O'Mara Books Limited,
9 Lion Yard, Tremadoc Road, London SW4 7NQ

W www.busterbooks.co.uk
f Buster Children's Books
🐦 @BusterBooks

Puzzles and solutions © Gareth Moore 2015

Illustrations and layouts © Buster Books 2015

A CIP catalogue record for this book is available from the British Library.

ISBN: 978-1-78055-308-5

2 4 6 8 10 9 7 5 3

Papers used by Buster Books are natural, recyclable products
made from wood grown in sustainable forests. The manufacturing processes
conform to the environmental regulations of the country of origin.

Printed and bound in January 2016 by CPI Group (UK) Ltd,
108 Beddington Lane, Croydon, CR0 4YY, United Kingdom

CROSS WORDS

for clever Kids

Buster Books

INTRODUCTION

Crosswords are the perfect puzzle challenge for clever kids. This book contains over 130 of them. They are divided into four levels of difficulty, and get tougher as the book progresses.

Beneath each puzzle grid you'll see a list of clues that you must solve. Each numbered clue corresponds to certain squares in the crossword grid. Once you have worked out the answer to a clue, write it in the correct space.

Sometimes, you'll be able to think of more than one answer to a clue. When this happens, wait until you solve some of the words that cross over that one in the grid, then use these letters to help you choose the correct solution.

Each clue has a number in brackets at the end, like this: (5). This shows you how many letters are in the word you are trying to guess and matches the number of empty squares in the grid. You might see two numbers, like this: (3, 3). This means that there are two words to place, each of the given length, such as 'One Day'. Don't leave a space between the words in the grid, though.

You might see '(inits)' after a clue. This means the answer is made up of the initial (first) letters of each word of the solution, for example 'OAP' for old age pensioner. You will also sometimes see '(abbr)' after a clue. This means that the solution is an abbreviated (shortened) form of a word, for example 'Dec' for December.

If you see a ';' in a clue, it means the clue is made up of different parts which will help you guess the solution.

If you get stuck on any word, the answers are at the back of the book, so you can take a sneak peak if you need to.

There's a 'Time' line at the top of every page for you to write in how long it took you to do each puzzle.

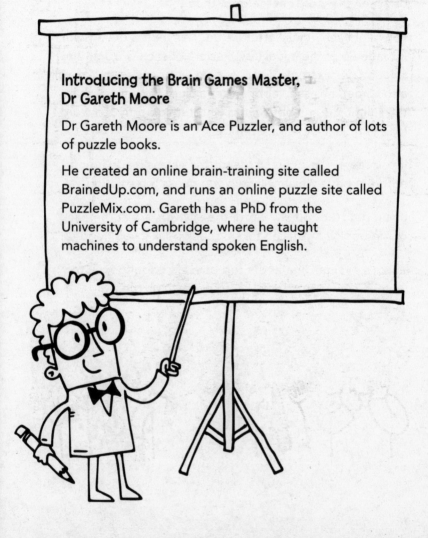

Introducing the Brain Games Master, Dr Gareth Moore

Dr Gareth Moore is an Ace Puzzler, and author of lots of puzzle books.

He created an online brain-training site called BrainedUp.com, and runs an online puzzle site called PuzzleMix.com. Gareth has a PhD from the University of Cambridge, where he taught machines to understand spoken English.

BEGINNER

 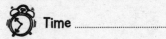
CROSSWORD 1

Across

3. Pop, rap or classical, for example (5)

5. Move as quickly as you can (3)

6. Bamboo-eating animal (5)

Down

1. In the countryside, away from town (5)

2. Really blowy outside, as in 'this is _ _ _ _ _ weather' (5)

4. The closest star to Earth (3)

CROSSWORD 2

Across

1. Past your bedtime, perhaps? (4)

3. Sugary sweet (5)

4. Newly-born child (4)

Down

1. A camel-like animal; anagram of 'a mall' (5)

2. The day after yesterday (5)

CROSSWORD 3

¹N	A	²M	E	■
E	■	A	■	³T
⁴W	A	T	E	R
T	■	C	■	E
■	⁵S	H	O	E

Across
1. Give a title to something (4)
4. What comes out when you turn the tap on (5)
5. Hard clothing you put on your foot (4)

Down
1. Type of lizard you might find in a garden pond (4)
2. Small stick struck to create a flame (5)
3. Very tall plant with branches and leaves (4)

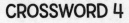

CROSSWORD 4

Across
1. Short version of 'Christmas' (4)
4. Once more (5)
5. Food often served to celebrate a birthday (4)

Down
2. Tricks done by a performer to impress people (5)
3. Thin branch or twig (5)

CROSSWORD 5

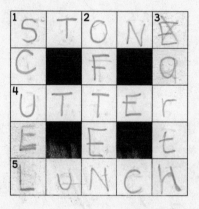

Across

1. Hard, solid rock; a pebble (5)
4. To say something (5)
5. Midday meal (5)

Down

1. The big bone inside your head (5)
2. Frequently (5)
3. Our planet (5)

CROSSWORD 6

Across

1. Symbol used to indicate addition (4)

4. A striped orange and black big cat, found in Asia (5)

5. A narrow road for walking along (4)

Down

2. Opposite of dark (5)

3. What you might call a male teacher (3)

4. Narrow end of something (3)

CROSSWORD 7

Across
1. Exam (4)

4. Keyboard instrument with black and white keys (5)

5. Middle part of your leg (4)

Down
1. Write using a computer keyboard (4)

2. Dirty mark on clothing (5)

3. Thick string, used for tying things up (4)

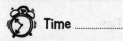

CROSSWORD 8

Across

1. Fall deeper and deeper underwater (4)

3. Loud breathing noise made during sleep (5)

4. Heat in an oven, especially for cakes and pastry (4)

Down

1. Father Christmas (5)

2. Someone who might assist doctors (5)

CROSSWORD 9

Across

1. A type of tree often seen in warm places (4)

4. The metal part of an ice skate (5)

5. Not looked after by people, as in 'a ____ animal' (4)

Down

1. Let someone do something; permit (5)

3. A small version of a larger object (5)

CROSSWORD 10

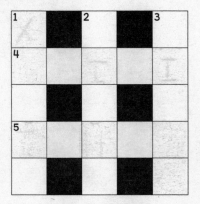

Across

4. Anxious; worried (5)

5. Teachers in a school (5)

Down

1. Someone who comes to visit (5)

2. Normal (5)

3. Hard; not easy to bend (5)

CROSSWORD 11

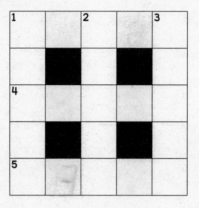

Across

1. Scary fairground ride: _ _ _ _ _ train (5)

4. Where a pop concert might take place (5)

5. Large sea creature with sharp teeth (5)

Down

1. Windows are made of this (5)

2. Theatre show with sung music (5)

3. Something trains run on (5)

CROSSWORD 12

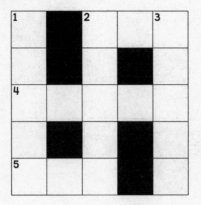

Across

2. A value of playing card; also an expert (3)

4. What you're writing on right now (5)

5. Say something that isn't true (3)

Down

1. Someone taught by a teacher (5)

2. Poisoned fruit given to Snow White (5)

3. A fault with a computer program (5)

CROSSWORD 13

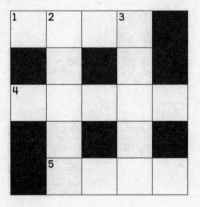

Across

1. Defrost; anagram of 'what' (4)

4. Honesty (5)

5. A sound that repeats (4)

Down

2. Animal used for riding (5)

3. Look at a television set (5)

CROSSWORD 14

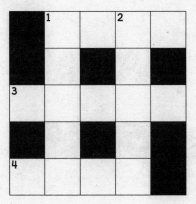

Across
1. A place selling food and drink (4)
3. 1000ml of liquid (5)
4. Have a desire, as in 'I
   ____ to do this' (4)

Down
1. Eastern country with the world's largest population (5)
2. In the gold-medal position (5)

 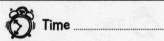
CROSSWORD 15

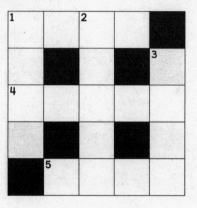

Across

1. A thin layer of dirt (4)

4. The shortest, widest finger (5)

5. Ancient instrument, like a small harp (4)

Down

1. Specific day in history when something happened (4)

2. Learn about something (5)

3. Woodwind instrument (4)

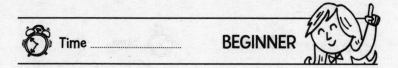
CROSSWORD 16

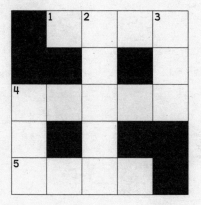

Across

1. Place where you can buy things (4)

4. A bog or marsh (5)

5. Mythical hairy snow monster (4)

Down

2. Organ for pumping blood around the body (5)

3. Popular music (3)

4. Nervous about talking to new people (3)

CROSSWORD 17

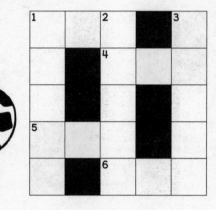

Across

1. Throw a ball high (3)

4. Move something back and forth against something else, as Aladdin did to make the genie appear (3)

5. Salt water covering a large part of the Earth (3)

6. The opposite of night (3)

Down

1. Rope for leading a dog (5)

2. Basic food made from flour (5)

3. Building where monks or nuns live (5)

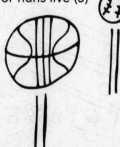

CROSSWORD 18

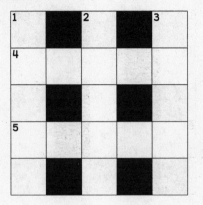

Across

4. Opposite of over; beneath something (5)

5. Turns over and over (5)

Down

1. Someone who protects a place (5)

2. No longer a child (5)

3. An item of clothing worn by women (5)

CROSSWORD 19

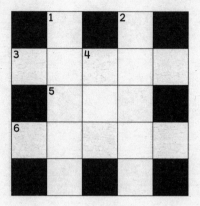

Across

3. A parish priest in the Church of England (5)

5. The fifth month of the year (3)

6. Absolutely necessary (5)

Down

1. Shy; easily scared (5)

2. A boat that's very similar to a canoe (5)

4. Common family pet (3)

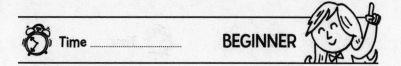
CROSSWORD 20

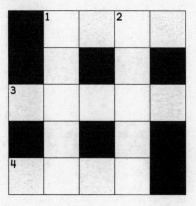

Across

1. A red, precious stone; the colour of the slippers in *The Wizard of Oz* (4)

3. Exactly right (5)

4. Something opened with a key (4)

Down

1. Cowboy contest (5)

2. Colour of coal (5)

CROSSWORD 21

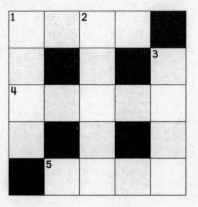

Across

1. Race around too quickly (4)

4. Flickering part of a fire (5)

5. Easy to break; not strong (4)

Down

1. Boat made of logs tied together (4)

2. Square, triangle or pentagon, for example (5)

3. The period from Monday to Sunday (4)

CROSSWORD 22

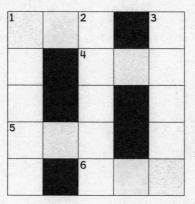

Across

1. The top half of your legs when sitting; where a cat might sit (3)

4. The whole lot (3)

5. Flying night-time animal (3)

6. How old you are (3)

Down

1. Entrance hall in a hotel or apartment block (5)

2. Spaghetti, lasagne or ravioli, for example (5)

3. Dish used to eat from (5)

CROSSWORD 23

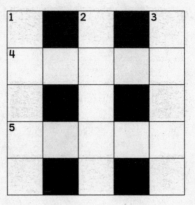

Across

4. Loud, non-musical sound (5)

5. Huge expanse of water (5)

Down

1. Vegetable that makes you cry (5)

2. Alarm on top of an ambulance or police car (5)

3. Trousers made of denim (5)

CROSSWORD 24

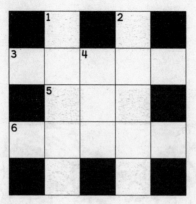

Across

3. Christmas song (5)

5. Something used to open locks (3)

6. Metal disc to commemorate an event (5)

Down

1. Without any clothes on (5)

2. Faithful (5)

4. Colour of a stop light (3)

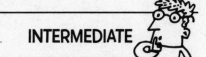

CROSSWORD 25

Across

2. Common waterbird with webbed feet (4)

4. A car with a driver whom you pay to take you somewhere (4)

5. Add some numbers; conclude a speech (3,2)

6. Where birds go to lay eggs (4)

7. Fix something that is broken (4)

Down

1. Edible tube of minced meat (7)

2. A precious jewel often used to decorate rings (7)

3. Write a piece of music (7)

CROSSWORD 26

Across

1. No person; no one (6)

4. Flowers growing on a fruit tree (7)

5. A sports player (7)

7. Hole on the surface of the moon (6)

Down

1. The tip of a pen (3)

2. Male sibling (7)

3. Sweet course of a meal (7)

6. To get something wrong is to ___ (3)

CROSSWORD 27

Across

3. A character of the alphabet (6)

4. Come first in a race (3)

5. Female equivalent of a king (5)

7. Person who treats sick animals (3)

8. Shiny Christmas decoration (6)

Down

1. A pop-up set of options on a computer (4)

2. House for a dog (6)

3. Water or oil, for example (6)

6. Whole numbers are either _____ or odd (4)

CROSSWORD 28

Across
2. Fried potatoes (5)
4. Weeks without any school (7)
5. Tap on a door (5)

Down
1. Tourist (7)
2. Something that tells the time (5)
3. A small, quick meal (5)

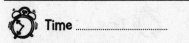

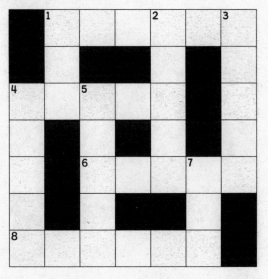

CROSSWORD 29

Across

1. Place where criminals are confined (6)

4. Work out a solution, as in '_ _ _ _ _ a puzzle' (5)

6. Third month of the year (5)

8. The part of your mouth you use for tasting (6)

Down

1. 'Turn the page' (inits) (3)

2. Make a promise (5)

3. Horse's whinny (5)

4. Clothing worn by a girl over the legs (5)

5. Bitter, yellow fruit; a slice of this is sometimes added to cola or other drinks (5)

7. Line of text used to prompt an actor (3)

CROSSWORD 30

Across

1. Type of tooth you get at the back of your mouth in your late teens (6)

4. The here and now (7)

6. A very small hair that you find on your eyelid (7)

8. Decorative cup awarded as a prize (6)

Down

1. Concern (5)

2. 'Emergency!' (inits) (3)

3. Wipe your feet on this (3)

5. Not very nice at all (5)

6. You must ___ and drink to stay alive (3)

7. The edge of a hole; part of your mouth (3)

CROSSWORD 31

Across

1. Stay away from (5)

5. Styles of clothes that people like (7)

6. Small, brown mark on skin (7)

7. Clean the floor with a broom (5)

Down

2. Car, boat or aeroplane, for example (7)

3. Draw a quick sketch (6)

4. Make less wide (6)

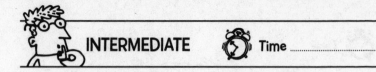

CROSSWORD 32

Across

1. Large, cruel giant (4)
4. A small wound (3)
6. Happy to wait (7)
7. Opposite of no (3)
8. Direction in which the sun rises (4)

Down

2. Group of stars (6)
3. When the moon moves in front of the sun (7)
5. Sport played at Wimbledon (6)

CROSSWORD 33

Across

2. For example, an apple, banana, mango or lemon (5)

4. Small carpet for wiping your feet on (7)

5. Move in time with music (5)

Down

1. Dried grape (7)

2. Overwhelm with water (5)

3. Draw over something by using another sheet of paper on top (5)

CROSSWORD 34

Across

1. Musical instrument played with fingers or a pick (6)

4. Building where plays are performed (7)

5. A pupil; someone who attends school (7)

7. Add salt and pepper to food (6)

Down

1. Instinctive thought: a ___ feeling (3)

2. Cold block you put in a drink (3,4)

3. Woman who plays a character in a film (7)

6. Make your skin turn darker in the sun (3)

CROSSWORD 35

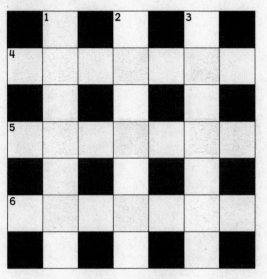

Across

4. A green jewel (7)

5. Thin, crispy biscuit (7)

6. Circus entertainer who leaps around (7)

Down

1. The United States (7)

2. Vehicle used on farms (7)

3. Something that is forbidden by law is _____ (7)

CROSSWORD 36

Across

1. Land by the sea (5)

4. Possess (3)

6. Motor vehicle (3)

7. You can travel quickly down a snowy slope by using two of these (3)

8. Bite sharply, like a dog might do (3)

9. Period of time that is an anagram of 'are' (3)

10. Male equivalent of daughter (3)

11. Spiky part of a plant (5)

Down

1. Potato snack (6)

2. Really old (7)

3. Violent windstorm (7)

5. Cloth used at mealtime to wipe your lips (6)

CROSSWORD 37

Across

1. Go without food, often for religious reasons (4)

3. Deity; a being that is worshipped (3)

5. To do very well at something (5)

6. At no time in the past or future (5)

7. Did own, as in 'I ___ that' (3)

8. Guernsey or Jersey, for example (4)

Down

1. The language that Parisians speak (6)

2. Silver medal position (6)

3. Clothing for hands used to keep you warm (6)

4. Unit for measuring an angle (6)

CROSSWORD 38

Across

1. First odd number greater than 1 (5)

4. Letters that mean 'very important person' (inits) (3)

6. Not dead (5)

7. Unable to see with your eyes (5)

8. Toilet (3)

9. Bet (5)

Down

1. Go from one place to another (6)

2. Red, orange, yellow, green, blue, indigo and violet (7)

3. Time when the sun sets (7)

5. Flour, dust and icing sugar are all examples of this (6)

CROSSWORD 39

Across

3. Outdoor meal (6)

4. Buddy; anagram of 'lap' (3)

5. Clever; intelligent; brainy (5)

7. Advanced in years (3)

8. Insect with hard covers over its wings (6)

Down

1. Thin layer covering a surface (4)

2. Small; not big (6)

3. Pale shade of a colour (6)

6. Small loaf of bread (4)

 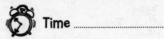
CROSSWORD 40

Across

1. Triangular Indian snack (6)

4. Damage; ruin something (7)

5. The way something tastes (7)

7. A man, woman or child (6)

Down

1. Not happy (3)

2. Something incorrect (7)

3. Solemn or thoughtful (7)

6. Did go for a run (3)

CROSSWORD 41

Across

2. Opposite of short (4)

4. Sharp-tasting, like lemons (4)

5. Piece of meat for roasting (5)

6. A type of black tea, ____ Grey (4)

7. Period of twelve months (4)

Down

1. A word meaning 'to do magic' (7)

2. Someone who teaches you sports or keep-fit (7)

3. A, B and C are _____ (7)

CROSSWORD 42

Across

4. Person who gives the lessons at school (7)

5. Lightweight waterproof coat (7)

6. Sports umpire (7)

Down

1. Belonging to the same family (7)

2. Halloween month (7)

3. Waterproof boots (7)

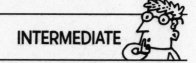

CROSSWORD 43

Across

1. More than enough; also an anagram of 'maple' (5)

4. A type of computer made by Apple (3)

6. Spoon used for serving ice cream (5)

7. 'L'-size clothing (5)

8. The opposite of hello (3)

9. Picture painted on the wall (5)

Down

1. Soak up liquid (6)

2. A task that requires a solution (7)

3. Ruler of multiple countries (7)

5. A typical breakfast food (6)

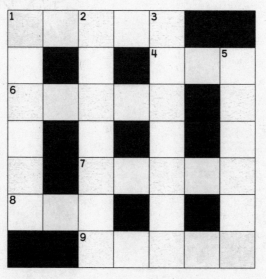

CROSSWORD 44

Across

1. Loft (5)

4. An abbreviation for 'old-age pensioner' (inits) (3)

6. Large water vessel, like you might serve tea in a cafeteria from (3)

7. Female bird (3)

8. Police officer (3)

9. Planned for a certain time (3)

10. The length of time that a person has been alive (3)

11. Used for drawing straight lines (5)

Down

1. If you have this you might need an inhaler (6)

2. Loud noise heard during a storm (7)

3. Not allow to be seen (7)

5. Hot-tasting, black spice used in cooking (6)

CROSSWORD 45

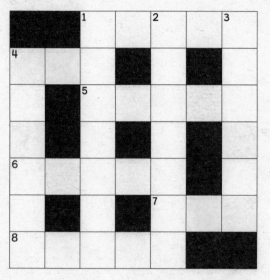

Across

1. Vision (5)

4. A dog's foot (3)

5. Foreigner from another planet (5)

6. Person in charge of a plane (5)

7. Type of fish which looks a bit like a snake (3)

8. A tall building, such as a skyscraper (5)

Down

1. Drink some liquid (7)

2. Shiny, powdery substance used in crafts (7)

3. Dig a passage (6)

4. Doll controlled by hand, sometimes with strings (6)

CROSSWORD 46

Across

1. Help (6)

4. The theoretical ring around the middle of the Earth (7)

5. A red sauce you might have with chips (7)

7. The colour of lemons (6)

Down

1. A gorilla, for example (3)

2. Transport back and forth (7)

3. Bag that is an anagram of 'latches' (7)

6. Wooden bench in a church (3)

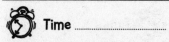 
CROSSWORD 47

Across

1. Desert waterhole (5)

4. Had some food (3)

6. Clothing worn over the front of the body to protect clothes (5)

7. Siren (5)

8. Tree whose name is an anagram of 'Mel' (3)

9. An artist uses this to prop up their painting (5)

Down

1. A common citrus fruit (6)

2. Family name (7)

3. Strapped shoes, often worn in summer (7)

5. The white surface of teeth (6)

CROSSWORD 48

Across

1. Glowing remains of a fire (6)

4. Let go of something (7)

6. Clothes worn in bed (7)

8. Cheddar, brie or stilton, for example (6)

Down

1. Each one of something (5)

2. Pollinating insect (3)

3. Look at something with your eyes (3)

5. Tool for digging the ground (5)

6. Publicly listed company (inits) (3)

7. Amazement (3)

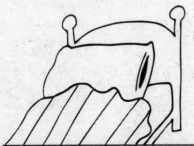

CROSSWORD 49

Across

3. Picture puzzle that requires assembly (6)

4. Movement of a dog's tail (3)

5. Small garden ornament with beard and pointed hat (5)

7. A rock with metal in it (3)

8. A monkey's favourite fruit? (6)

Down

1. Noticeboard that tells you which way to go (4)

2. Used for taking photographs (6)

3. South-American wildcat that looks like a leopard (6)

6. Religious man who lives in a monastery (4)

CROSSWORD 50

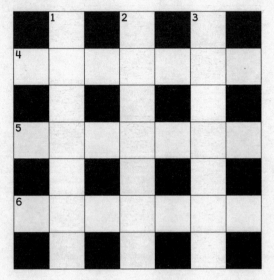

Across

4. The bad guy in a story (7)

5. Device for grilling bread (7)

6. Warm up your muscles before exercise (7)

Down

1. A type of sticky rice dish (7)

2. Spectacles (7)

3. Absolute quiet (7)

CROSSWORD 51

Across

1. The current subject that you're talking about (5)

4. When I leave the house to go out, I set ___ (3)

6. Rest on the surface of water; the opposite of sink (5)

7. Message sent from one computer to another (5)

8. Abbreviation for 'and other similar things' (3)

9. Something you enjoy; a reward (5)

Down

1. Sticky and chewy type of sweet (6)

2. A series of related tasks (7)

3. A creamy dairy product with lumps, '_____ cheese' (7)

5. Fish or meat with all the bones removed (6)

CROSSWORD 52

Across

1. Ask someone to come to an event, such as a party (6)

4. Bird associated with ice and snow (7)

5. Someone who is in the army (7)

7. Small, portable computer (6)

Down

1. Cheeky devil (3)

2. 'Plain' ice-cream flavour (7)

3. Somebody who is just visiting a place (7)

6. Type of fast-spoken music (3)

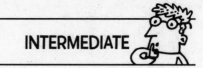
CROSSWORD 53

Across

1. Entertain someone and make them laugh (5)

5. First part of the day (7)

6. Place to catch a train (7)

7. Hair on a man's chin and cheeks (5)

Down

2. Huge and frightening creature (7)

3. Older than someone else (6)

4. A water container, usually made of plastic (6)

CROSSWORD 54

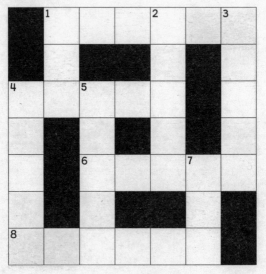

Across

1. Case to carry money in (6)

4. Injure (5)

6. Tidy up; neaten (5)

8. Make a rough drawing (6)

Down

1. Classic game, 'Guess ___?' (3)

2. Soup spoon (5)

3. Railway vehicle (5)

4. Flow of water on to a beach (5)

5. Your mum or dad's brother (5)

7. A type of tree, 'mountain ___' (3)

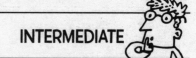

CROSSWORD 55

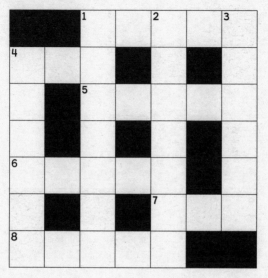

Across

1. One of Snow White's helpers (5)

4. That girl; her (3)

5. Special meal with lots of food for many people (5)

6. Red liquid flowing around your body (5)

7. Used for rowing (3)

8. Ancient Roman language (5)

Down

1. Thaw something out (7)

2. Leave behind (7)

3. Male parent (6)

4. A shape or sign that means something (6)

CROSSWORD 56

Across

1. The result of adding up some numbers (5)

4. Biblical couple, Adam and ___ (3)

6. Dry end of a sandwich (5)

7. Hold a video on its current picture (5)

8. Fasten; ___ your shoelaces (3)

9. The crime of stealing (5)

Down

1. You need a _____ to travel by bus or train (6)

2. Brass musical instrument (7)

3. Green, leafy salad vegetable (7)

5. Someone who knows a lot about a subject (6)

CROSSWORD 57

Across

2. Edible freshwater fish (5)

4. Dracula, for example (7)

5. What you bite your food with (5)

Down

1. Difficult; complicated (7)

2. A grilled slice of bread (5)

3. Small handheld lamp (5)

CROSSWORD 58

Across

1. A sworn promise (4)

4. A goal or target (3)

6. Sweet dessert (7)

7. Meal eaten in the afternoon (3)

8. Female child (4)

Down

2. Eighth month (6)

3. A lady's carry bag (7)

5. Jesus' bed in the Nativity story (6)

CROSSWORD 59

Across

1. Weapon with a long, pointed blade (5)

5. Gather (7)

6. He pulls Santa's sleigh (7)

7. Precious stone (5)

Down

2. Greet on arrival (7)

3. To find out how to make food you can check a _____ (6)

4. How loud something is (6)

CROSSWORD 60

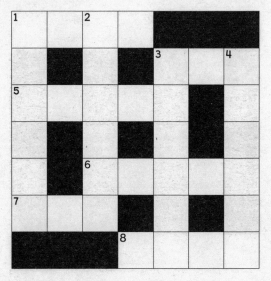

Across

1. Thing to be done (4)

3. Have a small amount of a drink (3)

5. Place where a bird sits (5)

6. New and original; unusual (5)

7. Shelled food often eaten fried, scrambled or boiled (3)

8. A black bird, often noisy (4)

Down

1. Walk quietly on your toes (6)

2. Coiled spiral of metal wire (6)

3. Shake with cold (6)

4. Cushion on a bed (6)

CROSSWORD 61

Across

2. Likely to vomit (4)

4. The opposite of shallow (4)

5. Feeling of fear (5)

6. Group or society (4)

7. If you have a rash on your skin it may do this (4)

Down

1. A large snake (7)

2. Leafy, green vegetable that Popeye eats (7)

3. Milk contains _____, which is good for bones and teeth (7)

CROSSWORD 62

Across

2. Come into flower (5)

4. Repeated visual design (7)

5. Opposite of light (5)

Down

1. Person who delivers letters (7)

2. Sandy area beside the sea (5)

3. Kindness and pity (5)

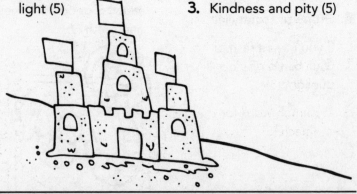

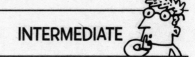

CROSSWORD 63

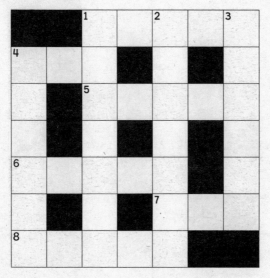

Across

1. Large bird that is a symbol of the USA (5)

4. Cardboard container (3)

5. Phones someone up (5)

6. Fruit used for making wine (5)

7. Thin beam of sunlight (3)

8. Common word for the stomach (5)

Down

1. Shout out (7)

2. Place to display art (7)

3. Unusual, often from another part of the world (6)

4. Intelligent (6)

 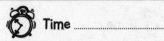
CROSSWORD 64

Across

1. Dried grape, like a currant or sultana (6)

4. Powerful ape found in central Africa (7)

5. Imagine something is real (7)

7. Thin paper used for blowing your nose (6)

Down

1. Thick blanket for the floor (3)

2. A resident of Tel Aviv (7)

3. An affliction, such as a cold (7)

6. Become dead (3)

CROSSWORD 65

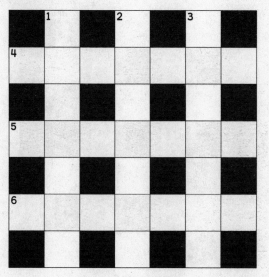

Across

4. Diary (7)

5. Post sent around the world by plane (7)

6. Young goose (7)

Down

1. Line where the sky meets the Earth (7)

2. Shake with fear (7)

3. Brave; courageous (7)

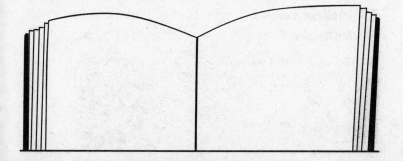

CROSSWORD 66

Across

1. Female children; not boys but _____ (5)

4. The 'p' in m.p.h. on a car dashboard (3)

6. Newspapers and television in general (5)

7. Small boat with a paddle (5)

8. The day of the week Pancake Day's on, in short (3)

9. Not clean (5)

Down

1. Outfit for school sports (3,3)

2. Decreased (7)

3. You use this tool to tighten nuts (7)

5. Cure for an illness (6)

ADVANCED

CROSSWORD 67

Across

1. The final 'w' in the Internet abbreviation 'www' (3)
3. Hit something gently (3)
5. If your head hurts, you say you have a head_____ (4)
7. A word that means 'more than usually', as in ,'you are _____ special' (5)
9. Grown-up boys (3)
10. A photo, for example (5)
11. Something some people catch to school (3)
12. Man who plays a character in a film (5)
15. Common edible fish, sometimes used in sandwiches (4)
16. A model car or a board game, for example (3)
17. The opposite to a shake of the head (3)

Down

1. Substance found inside your ear (3)
2. A metal pole (3)
3. Violent storm; also the name of a play by Shakespeare, 'The _____' (7)
4. Big black leopard (7)
6. Holiday vehicle for camping (7)
7. A display (7)
8. Needing a drink (7)
13. Metal food container (3)
14. Opposite of even (3)

CROSSWORD 68

Across

1. The name of one of Santa's reindeer (5)
4. In support of (3)
6. Electronic device used to cook food (9)
7. Strong wind which spins everything around (9)
10. Legolas in *Lord of the Rings* (3)
11. Map shaped like a ball (5)

Down

1. Large, edible mollusc with two shells of equal size (4)
2. Troublesome behaviour (8)
3. Three; anagram of 'riot' (4)
4. Pink wading bird (8)
5. A cereal plant; an anagram of 'rey' (3)
7. Sorrow; misfortune (3)
8. Organ used for breathing (4)
9. Be brave enough to do something (4)

CROSSWORD 69

Across
1. The sound a snake makes (4)
4. Hard part at the end of your finger (4)
7. Settee (4)
8. A short message or letter; a musical sound (4)
9. Carved pumpkin festival (9)
12. Identical (4)
14. Brainwave (4)
16. You put this in a sink to stop the water draining (4)
17. At the end of your arm (4)

Down
1. Owns (3)
2. Small garden creature with a hard shell on its back (5)
3. Break a law, especially a religious one (3)
5. Romantic feeling (4)
6. Selfish; not generous (4)
9. Say this to ask people to be quiet (4)
10. Type of light that usually has a base and a shade (4)
11. Stand something on scales (5)
13. Large-horned deer (3)
15. If you cut yourself, you may need first ___ (3)

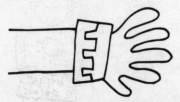

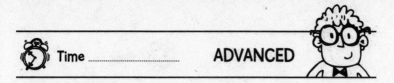
CROSSWORD 70

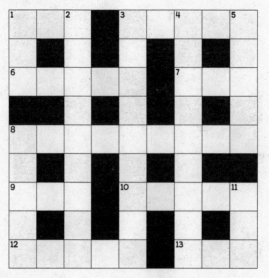

Across

1. Opposite of dry (3)
3. Book of maps (5)
6. The main part of your body that is attached to both your legs and arms (5)
7. Shout of disapproval, or shout this at someone to scare them! (3)
8. A letter of the alphabet that isn't a vowel (9)
9. Large, ostrich-like bird (3)
10. Really silly person (5)
12. A fright (5)
13. Religious woman who lives in a convent (3)

Down

1. Clever humour (3)
2. Big, poisonous, hairy spider (9)
3. Say sorry (9)
4. Someone who catalogues books (9)
5. The opposite of tall (5)
8. Board game with kings, queens and pawns (5)
11. The number of fingers and thumbs you have (3)

CROSSWORD 71

Across

4. The middle, hinged part of your arm (5)
6. Round object used in games (4)
7. For what reason? (3)
9. Details of where someone lives (7)
10. Something you sleep on (3)
12. Famous science-fiction series, 'Star ____' (4)
13. Tag (5)

Down

1. Tune (6)
2. A decorative knot in a ribbon (3)
3. A light brown colour that is also the name of a sweet (7)
5. Speak secretly (7)
8. Device for boiling water (6)
11. Block the flow of water (3)

CROSSWORD 72

Across

1. School subject involving numbers (5)
4. Lamb's mother (3)
6. Often used to get from one floor to another in a shopping mall (9)
7. Type of beach chair (9)
10. Two of these are used when you look at the world (3)
11. Sound made by a sheep or goat (5)

Down

1. More than one mouse (4)
2. Vehicle with three wheels (8)
3. Loose earth (4)
4. Opposite of 'exit' (8)
5. Essential for listening (3)
7. Female deer (3)
8. Seaside rock pool animal (4)
9. The underground part of a plant (4)

CROSSWORD 73

Across

1. Christian building of worship (6)
4. Average score on a golf hole (3)
5. Available for business, especially if a shop (4)
7. Visual display unit, such as a computer screen (inits) (3)
10. Green lawn plant (5)
11. The blue area above the ground (3)
13. Building blocks or action figures, for example (4)
16. The closing to a story, 'The ___' (3)
17. Decorative streaked stone, often used in buildings (6)

Down

1. Weep (3)
2. Alien spaceship (inits) (3)
3. Wanting food (6)
4. A pile of blank paper fastened together in a book (3)
6. Succeed at a test or exam (4)
7. Someone who has suffered harm (6)
8. The ____ Duckling (4)
9. Noticed something; I ___ it happen (3)
12. Tease (3)
14. Underwater boat (3)
15. The cost for something (3)

CROSSWORD 74

Across

1. Hard covering over a healing cut or graze (4)
4. Competition to arrive first (4)
7. A Jedi master in the *Star Wars* films (4)
8. Something you obey (4)
9. This puzzle (9)
12. Not fooled by; 'I'm __ __ you' (2,2)
14. The sun, for example; there are lots of these in the night sky (4)
16. Small mark (4)
17. School test (4)

Down

1. Utter a word or sentence (3)
2. A metal made from copper and zinc; 'as bold as _____' (5)
3. Video cassette recorder (inits) (3)
5. The name of the money used in most European countries (4)
6. A plant growing where it isn't wanted (4)
9. Cage or house for chickens (4)
10. Cereal ingredient in porridge (4)
11. Rubbish (5)
13. Anagram of 'pot' and of 'top' (3)
15. Bash a door with a large piece of wood (3)

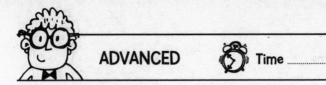

CROSSWORD 75

Across

4. When you think about something and make a deduction, you use _____; also a type of puzzle (5)
6. Small, wriggling creature (4)
7. A group of related items (3)
9. Person who treats teeth (7)
10. The back part of a soccer goal (3)
12. Sound made by a dog (4)
13. Like a TV without pictures (5)

Down

1. A flat, oval-shaped nut (6)
2. That man or boy's (3)
3. Young child who has started to walk (7)
5. A period of one hundred years (7)
8. Decoration for a present (6)
11. Playground game where one person chases the rest (3)

CROSSWORD 76

Across

1. Two of these on a car windscreen help keep it clean (5)
4. Large container for liquids (3)
6. Mixed up (9)
7. Bad dream (9)
10. Oxygen or nitrogen, for example (3)
11. Sit down on your knees (5)

Down

1. Where spiders live (4)
2. The Queen can give these honours to people who please her (8)
3. Space, as in 'they have ____ for us (4)
4. Worth a lot of money (8)
5. A word that's short for 'teddy' (3)
7. Repeatedly bother or scold someone (3)
8. Mark used when something is correct (4)
9. The opposite of good (4)

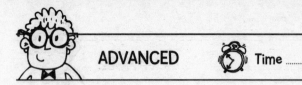
CROSSWORD 77

Across

1. Not many (3)
3. Getting ___ and about helps you stay fit (3)
5. How meat is before it is cooked (3)
7. An even number just less than three (3)
8. Lazy start to the day (3,2)
10. Flash during a thunderstorm (9)
13. Juicy tropical fruit (5)
16. Did light, as in 'I ___ the candle' (3)
18. In the past; 'it happened long ___ (3)
19. Deep frying pan used to make Chinese food (3)
20. The whole number between zero and two (3)

Down

1. Greasy substance on meat, such as the rind on bacon (3)
2. Not right (5)
3. Bird that calls 'too-wit too-woo' (3)
4. The definite article, as in 'that's ___ one I want' (3)
6. Warm and comfortable (4)
9. Small hotel where you can spend the night (3)
10. Walk with difficulty, as you might do if you twisted an ankle (4)
11. Squeeze lovingly (3)
12. Eskimo's house (5)
14. Not previously existing (3)
15. Tree that produces acorns (3)
17. There are five at the end of your foot (3)

CROSSWORD 78

Across

1. Jumping insect that attaches itself to dogs and cats (4)
4. Legend (4)
7. Lacking in sensation (4)
8. Scream at someone (4)
9. Every person (9)
12. Large, decorative type of flower that's usually purple or yellow (4)
14. You might say this if you stub your toe (4)
16. Low-pitch musical instrument (4)
17. Slightly wet (4)

Down

1. Amusement (3)
2. Middle traffic light colour (5)
3. Place where pigs live (3)
5. Person who does something brave (4)
6. Button you press to start a film (4)
9. A long and famous story (4)
10. Make changes (4)
11. Wide (5)
13. The result of adding some numbers (3)
15. The fruit of a rose (3)

CROSSWORD 79

Across

4. To try to win a game by breaking the rules (5)
6. Market (4)
7. Opposite of wet (3)
9. Unusual; different (7)
10. Larger than normal size (3)
12. Joy; delight (4)
13. A single leaf of a flower (5)

Down

1. Surface on which films are projected (6)
2. Father (3)
3. Yellow root vegetable (7)
5. You put food in this at the supermarket (7)
8. Small titter or laugh (6)
11. Jelly-like substance (3)

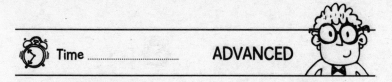
CROSSWORD 80

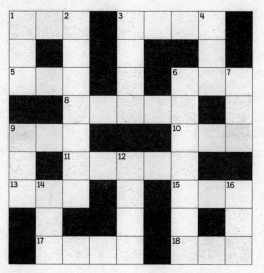

Across

1. Substance used to colour hair or clothes (3)
3. Use this when you wash your hands (4)
5. Used to exist (3)
6. Someone who loves a band or team (3)
8. You dry your face or hands with this (5)
9. Stopping at en route, as in 'The train went from London to Bristol ___ Swindon' (3)
10. Black, liquid fuel extracted from the ground (3)
11. Long, narrow tube for drinking (5)
13. When asking directions, you might say 'Which ___ do I go?' (3)
15. Flow back; also an anagram of 'beb' (3)
17. Object in the sky that causes tides (4)
18. Drop to a lower level (3)

Down

1. Drops of water formed on cool surfaces during the night (3)
2. Fantastic feeling (7)
3. Opposite of fast (4)
4. Podded vegetable (3)
6. Comes into bloom (7)
7. A score of zero (3)
9. Solemn promise (3)
12. Water falling from the sky (4)
14. Between your shoulder and your hand (3)
16. Creepy-crawly (3)

 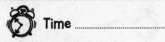

CROSSWORD 81

Across

1. Rest in bed (5)
4. Briefly place something into a liquid and then take it back out (3)
6. Long word for spying; the use of spies (9)
7. Spotty mushroom (9)
10. A light touch of the hand (3)
11. A person from Greece (5)

Down

1. Store a document on a computer (4)
2. Large, grey animal with big ears and a trunk (8)
3. Type of shirt; also a swimming pool game, water ____ (4)
4. Conversation (8)
5. Mince ___, eaten at Christmas (3)
7. The highest part of something (3)
8. Animal that's an anagram of 'tags' (4)
9. Wish someone good ____ for a test (4)

CROSSWORD 82

Across

1. Game with black tiles decorated with white dots representing numbers (8)
5. Informal word for a man (3)
6. Snack food often served with hamburgers (5)
8. Animal's footwear used as a sign of good luck (9)
10. Long seat for several people (5)
13. Rules of a country (3)
15. Heavy fall of rain (8)

Down

1. Common family pet (3)
2. Town dignitary (5)
3. Your and my (3)
4. Try to get money from someone through a legal process; also a girl's name (3)
6. Opposite of stale (5)
7. Female equivalent of 'he' (3)
8. Device for plugging multiple electronic devices into (3)
9. Opposite of goodbye (5)
11. A Muslim festival (3)
12. Farmyard animal that produces milk (3)
14. Period of fighting between armies (3)

CROSSWORD 83

Across

4. Type of sad jazz music (5)
6. Number of sides a rectangle has (4)
7. The day before Friday, in short (3)
9. Common white or grey seabird (7)
10. Ate (3)
12. A piece of land (4)
13. Relating to a king or queen (5)

Down

1. In a foreign country (6)
2. Joined someone at an agreed place (3)
3. Red edible shellfish with two big claws (7)
5. The _____ end of a swimming pool is the less deep end (7)
8. Colour made by mixing red and blue (6)
11. A small mark, like a full stop (3)

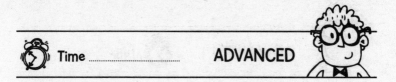
CROSSWORD 84

Across

1. Final calendar month (abbr) (3)
3. Somewhere where lots of food is grown (4)
5. Somewhere people go to keep fit (3)
6. Came first in a race (3)
8. Baked dough covered with cheese, tomato and other toppings (5)
9. Word that means 'as well' and rhymes with 'two' (3)
10. Use oars to move a boat (3)
11. White granules sometimes added to sweeten tea or coffee (5)
13. Brazil, hazel and almond are all examples of this (3)
15. Covered in ice (3)
17. The opposite of an entrance (4)
18. Letters you might find written on a gravestone (inits) (3)

Down

1. Make a hole in the ground with a spade (3)
2. Decayed grass and leaves used to help plants grow (7)
3. What a drink of cola does when poured into a glass (4)
4. Barnyard sound (3)
6. Someone who fights in battle (7)
7. At once (3)
9. Heavy unit of weight (3)
12. Butting animal (4)
14. Operate; an anagram of 'sue' (3)
16. The sound a small dog makes when it barks (3)

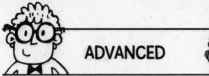

CROSSWORD 85

Across

1. Trainee soldier; also an anagram of 'acted' (5)
4. Purchase an item (3)
6. Mark left by a step (9)
7. Type of music composed by people such as Mozart (9)
10. Thick black liquid used for surfacing roads (3)
11. Stick something in place (5)

Down

1. Someone who cooks food for you at a restaurant (4)
2. For example, Tyrannosaurus rex or Stegosaurus (8)
3. Something designed to catch you out (4)
4. Daughter of a king and queen (8)
5. Up until now; I haven't told anyone ___ (3)
7. Baby's bed (3)
8. What a square shape on a video player button means (4)
9. Happening at this moment, especially on TV (4)

CROSSWORD 86

Across

1. The magician pulled a _____ out of his hat! (6)
4. Illness often caught in the winter (3)
5. Mix a liquid (4)
7. Casual goodbye (3)
10. Welsh breed of dog (5)
11. Month between April and June (3)
13. The world's second-largest cat, after the tiger (4)
16. Have a need to give money to someone (3)
17. Building where a god is worshipped (6)

Down

1. A fast jog (3)
2. Public-transport vehicle (3)
3. Large bird that gobbles (6)
4. Travel through the air (3)
6. Cut away unwanted parts, for example with scissors (4)
7. Type of gymnastic dance (6)
8. Repeat the same sound again (4)
9. Have a go at an activity (3)
12. Large monkey without a tail (3)
14. Short sleep (3)
15. Tool used for scraping weeds (3)

CROSSWORD 87

Across
4. Special prize given for achievement (5)
6. Long, pointed animal tooth (4)
7. Useful piece of information (3)
9. Standard outfit everyone at the same place wears (7)
10. Do something wrongly (3)
12. Parent's sister (4)
13. Type of boat with sails (5)

Down
1. Bird that likes shiny objects (6)
2. Drawings, paintings, sculptures and music (3)
3. First month of the year (7)
5. A four-sided shape used on playing cards (7)
8. Fruit used to make ketchup (6)
11. Was in charge (3)

CROSSWORD 88

Across

1. Large bird that can run fast but can't fly (7)
6. A long period of history (3)
7. Common Italian food made of egg and flour (5)
8. Police officer (9)
10. The hard seed in a cherry or peach (5)
12. Grow old (3)
13. Person being treated by a doctor (7)

Down

1. Cloudy (8)
2. Vehicle that travels on rails (5)
3. Unable to wait (9)
4. Possesses (3)
5. A paved area or surface (8)
9. Sharp part of a knife (5)
11. Elderly person (inits) (3)

CROSSWORD 89

Across
1. Sorrow; trouble; upset (8)
5. Sheep's bleat (3)
6. Breakable, clear material (5)
8. Celebration on 14th February, Saint _____'s Day (9)
10. Quiet; calm (5)
13. Chew food and swallow (3)
15. Something to keep you dry during rain (8)

Down
1. Touch gently with a tissue in order to clean or dry (3)
2. Opposite of big (5)
3. Slippery fish (3)
4. 'Help needed!' (inits) (3)
6. Appears when you rub a lamp in some fairy tales (5)
7. Understand, as in 'I ___' (3)
8. Special person; celebrity (inits) (3)
9. Perfect (5)
11. Large, flightless bird that's native to Australia (3)
12. Young of a tiger, lion or bear (3)
14. Hot, brewed drink (3)

CROSSWORD 90

Across

1. Part of your body you kiss with (4)
3. Choose, as in '____ one of these' (4)
5. Bag for school books (7)
9. 'Look on the other side' (inits) (3)
10. Poisonous snake (5)
11. Deep groove made by wheels (3)
12. Final course of a meal (7)
16. Cruel; horrible; unkind (4)
17. In addition to (4)

Down

1. African big cat with spotted coat (7)
2. Large expanse of water between countries (3)
3. Public limited company (inits) (3)
4. Stick used to play pool or billiards (3)
5. You wear these inside your shoes (5)
6. Furniture you might eat at (5)
7. Red playing-card suit (5)
8. The characters that make up the alphabet (7)
13. 24th December is Christmas ___ (3)
14. What the Earth orbits (3)
15. Knock quickly (3)

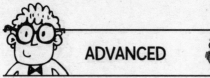
CROSSWORD 91

Across

1. White piano keys used to be made of this (5)
4. A small quantity of a drink (3)
6. Someone who travels into space (9)
7. Medical care (9)
10. Put water on (3)
11. Narrow street or passage (5)

Down

1. Concept (4)
2. Cream used for healing skin (8)
3. Round spinning toy (2,2)
4. Disgraceful (8)
5. A corgi, if you're the Queen (3)
7. Pull one vehicle with another (3)
8. Large, edible fish (4)
9. Not very big at all (4)

CROSSWORD 92

Across

1. Someone who studies at university (7)
6. Number not wholly divisible by 2 (3)
7. Large wildcat with black stripes (5)
8. Bird in the pear tree? (9)
10. Mozart's 'The Magic Flute' for example (5)
12. Short version of 'internet' (3)
13. Hide (7)

Down

1. Desert creature with a sting in its tail (8)
2. Opposite of over (5)
3. To amuse someone (9)
4. Powerful boat used for pulling ships (3)
5. From Eastern countries such as Japan or China (8)
9. For example, a waltz or a tango (5)
11. Abbreviation that means 'and so on' (3)

CROSSWORD 93

Across

1. White flakes that fall from the sky (4)
4. Region or space, as in 'that's part of the play ____' (4)
7. Examination (4)
8. Mark left after an injury has healed (4)
9. Tree that stays green all year long (9)
12. Go quickly; hurry (4)
14. Free from contamination (4)
16. Dogs can wag this (4)
17. Yellow part of an egg (4)

Down

1. Rest your bottom on a chair (3)
2. When it rains, _____ falls from the sky (5)
3. Word for agreeing (3)
5. Home of Winnie the Pooh, 'Hundred ____ Wood' (4)
6. Remove creases from clothing (4)
9. British nobleman (4)
10. The opposite direction to West (4)
11. Response (5)
13. Did own (3)
15. Large type of deer (3)

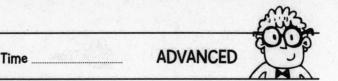

CROSSWORD 94

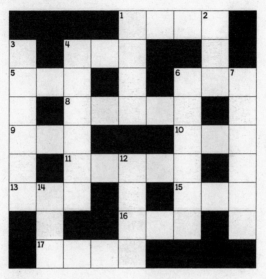

Across

1. Black playing-card suit (4)
4. Laughing, via SMS (inits) (3)
5. Cereal used in bread and biscuits (3)
6. Small bang (3)
8. Tall, narrow building (5)
9. The opposite of something, as in ,'I will do this but ___ that' (3)
10. Everyone (3)
11. The opposite of full (5)
13. Female equivalent of 'his' (3)
15. Part of your body used to see (3)
16. Way to address a knight (3)
17. Finned creature that lives in water (4)

Down

1. An animal's sharp, curved nail (4)
2. Noise made by a ghost (3)
3. Something from France (6)
4. Message sent by post (6)
6. Words you address to God (6)
7. Powder inside a flower (6)
12. Move something away from you (4)
14. Dobby, in *Harry Potter* (3)

CROSSWORD 95

Across

1. Show affection using your lips (4)
3. Something you eat (4)
5. A green precious stone (7)
9. Common road vehicle (3)
10. Really surprise (5)
11. And not, as in 'neither this ___ that' (3)
12. Gift (7)
16. Not pleasant to look at (4)
17. A bird's home (4)

Down

1. Tomato sauce (7)
2. The total amount (3)
3. On behalf of (3)
4. Nocturnal bird of prey (3)
5. Use a rubber on paper (5)
6. Avoid (5)
7. Someone who looks after a celebrity and finds them jobs (5)
8. Unfreeze (7)
13. Old piece of cloth (3)
14. Where the sun, moon and stars are (3)
15. Religious woman (3)

CROSSWORD 96

Across

1. A letter of the alphabet which isn't a consonant (5)
4. Not on (3)
6. Soft, cuddly toy (5,4)
7. High-ranking teacher (9)
10. Not tell the truth (3)
11. Untidy; dirty (5)

Down

1. Underwear worn on your top half to keep you warm (4)
2. Cupboard for hanging clothes (8)
3. A polite way to refer to a woman (4)
4. Abroad (8)
5. A long way (3)
7. Friend (3)
8. Academic test (4)
9. A red precious stone (4)

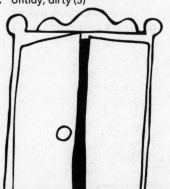

CROSSWORD 97

Across

4. Bed covering (5)
6. Joint where your leg bends (4)
7. Overhead shot in tennis (3)
9. Give a warning (7)
10. Limb connected to your shoulder (3)
12. Edge of something (4)
13. Person trained to look after sick people (5)

Down

1. Of use (6)
2. Substance used to style hair (3)
3. Mythical one-horned animal (7)
5. Whirlwind (7)
8. Glittery material used to decorate Christmas trees (6)
11. Attack and rob someone (3)

CROSSWORD 98

Across

1. Ball game similar to rounders (8)
5. Make a knot in a strip of material (3)
6. Something taken with a camera (5)
8. Someone who works without being paid (9)
10. Somewhere where sports events take place (5)
13. Practical joke (3)
15. Thick, spongy part of a bed (8)

Down

1. Used to play cricket (3)
2. Odour (5)
3. A boy's name that's also an anagram of 'has' (3)
4. Did light (3)
6. Black-and-white bear-like animal found in China (5)
7. Paddle used to row a boat (3)
8. Going through; stopping at (3)
9. Large bird of prey (5)
11. Male sheep (3)
12. Louse often found in hair (3)
14. Oxygen or hydrogen, for example (3)

CROSSWORD 99

Across

1. The end part of a cable which you push into a socket (4)
4. Part of a plant that grows in the ground (4)
7. And this thing, too (4)
8. A steady look or stare (4)
9. Group of people living in one place (9)
12. Male equivalent of a queen (4)
14. In length units, there are twelve of these in a foot (4)
16. Children play with these (4)
17. Alter (4)

Down

1. Round, green vegetable that grows in a pod (3)
2. Someone marrying a bride (5)
3. Canine animal (3)
5. A car you hire to go somewhere (4)
6. To a great amount, as in 'she was ____ happy' (4)
9. Sweet, bread-like food (4)
10. Herb often used to season lamb (4)
11. Sound (5)
13. Obtained (3)
15. Small house or shelter (3)

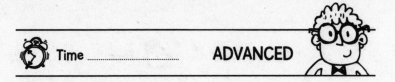
CROSSWORD 100

Across

1. Male equivalent of 'her' (3)
3. Small horse (4)
5. Nothing; zero (3)
6. Something you bathe in (3)
8. Soil; ground (5)
9. To beat your opponents (3)
10. Object laid by birds, fish, reptiles and insects (3)
11. Delicate pottery (5)
13. The smallest whole number above zero (3)
15. Something that controls the flow of water (3)
17. Bird often used to represent peace (4)
18. The point where something stops (3)

Down

1. Female bird, such as a chicken (3)
2. The absence of any sound (7)
3. Group two things together (4)
4. If I like someone, I might say 'I like ___' (3)
6. Place to see a play (7)
7. Opposite of small (3)
9. Which person? (3)
12. Lazy (4)
14. Head movement used to agree (3)
16. Seat covering (3)

CROSSWORD 101

Across

4. Turns over and over, as a ball does when it is moving along the ground (5)
6. The Abominable Snowman (4)
7. Name for your mother (3)
9. Wicked person (7)
10. Small, crawling insect (3)
12. Tall, rounded roof (4)
13. The overall amount (5)

Down

1. Pudding made with custard, cream, fruit and sponge (6)
2. Tall tree with broad leaves (3)
3. Person who works for someone else, often in their home (7)
5. A person's last name (7)
8. Seat put on a horse before riding (6)
11. Spinning toy (3)

CROSSWORD 102

Across

1. Long, soft seat for more than one person (4)
3. A very young child (4)
5. Small house in the country (7)
9. Sound made by a cow (3)
10. A fully-grown person (5)
11. Thick liquid used to fry food (3)
12. Tenth month (7)
16. Lump in a piece of string or rope (4)
17. Kitchen, lounge or hall (4)

Down

1. Soap for washing your hair (7)
2. 'Once upon a time, a long time ___' (3)
3. Closed the teeth on something (3)
4. What you put your shopping in (3)
5. Seashore; beach (5)
6. There is one of these on your hand (5)
7. Person in a play (5)
8. To shout out (7)
13. To be able; ' ___ do this' (3)
14. Not at home (3)
15. Part of the body used for listening (3)

CROSSWORD 103

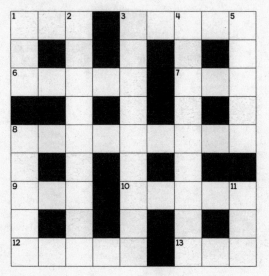

Across

1. Used to be (3)
3. A detailed plan or map (5)
6. Long-necked musical instrument with strings to pluck (5)
7. Unidentified flying object (inits) (3)
8. Result of a bomb going off (9)
9. Juice inside a tree (3)
10. Living; existing (5)
12. Big; sizeable (5)
13. Gang or crowd who are hard to control (3)

Down

1. Spider's home (3)
2. Rough paper used to smooth wood (9)
3. Can be milk, dark or white (9)
4. Silver-coloured metal, light in weight (9)
5. Sharp point growing on a rose stem (5)
8. Canvas stand used while painting (5)
11. The tide's movement away from the land (3)

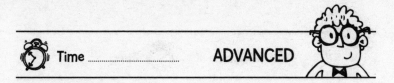
CROSSWORD 104

Across

1. Part of a bird used for flying (4)
4. Machine for weaving cloth (4)
7. A group of three people (4)
8. From 1st January to 31st December (4)
9. Slim dog, often used for racing (9)
12. Outdoor event with rides (4)
14. Number wholly divisible by 2 (4)
16. Sweet, brown, fizzy drink (4)
17. Small type of water lizard (4)

Down

1. Intelligence; cleverness (3)
2. Fame; honour (5)
3. Shy or modest (3)
5. Restaurant choices (4)
6. Poke or jab someone (4)
9. Special present for someone (4)
10. A story of heroic adventure (4)
11. Large sea (5)
13. A straight line of people (3)
15. Fruit with a hard shell (3)

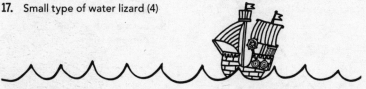

CROSSWORD 105

Across

1. Jewellery worn around the neck (8)
5. TV company, 'British Broadcasting Corporation' (inits) (3)
6. Not ever (5)
8. Dark-coloured songbird (9)
10. Food made in loaves (5)
13. Mischievous pixie (3)
15. Animal that hunts other animals (8)

Down

1. Metal point on a pen (3)
2. Chocolate powder (5)
3. Playing card '1' (3)
4. Female sheep (3)
6. Bare (5)
7. Colour of blood (3)
8. Float gently up and down in water (3)
9. Foolish person (5)
11. Tear something, such as a piece of paper (3)
12. You would use this if you wanted to cut down a tree (3)
14. For each, as in 'one ___ person' (3)

CROSSWORD 106

Across

4. Book for collecting photos or stamps (5)
6. Place where a wild animal lives (4)
7. Farm animal with a snout and a curly tail (3)
9. Collection of writing on a topic (7)
10. Bend the head as a sign of respect (3)
12. Cook in an oven (4)
13. Book containing a story (5)

Down

1. A pirate's bird (6)
2. You drink tea from this (3)
3. Spear used to catch whales (7)
5. Error (7)
8. Small, rounded stone (6)
11. Succeeded at a competition (3)

CROSSWORD 107

Across

1. Spiky-leaved plant with red berries (5)
4. Came across someone (3)
6. How someone signs their name (9)
7. Long, stringy pasta (9)
10. Needing to be paid (3)
11. The position between ninth and eleventh (5)

Down

1. Snake noise (4)
2. English, French or Spanish, for example (8)
3. A relaxation exercise where you hold various body positions (4)
4. Very high hill with a peak (8)
5. A common word you use to specify a particular object, instead of 'a' or 'an' (3)
7. Unhappy (3)
8. Sound made by an owl (4)
9. Scratch (4)

CROSSWORD 108

Across

1. Type of music, often associated with the saxophone (4)
4. The way out (4)
7. Take hold of something roughly (4)
8. Opposite of false (4)
9. White Arctic bear (5,4)
12. The sun, for example (4)
14. Slightly open (4)
16. A ticket in or out of a place (4)
17. Message sent to a mobile phone (4)

Down

1. A lively dance, especially an Irish one (3)
2. Black-and-white African horse (5)
3. Deep hole in the ground (3)
5. Large plant with a trunk (4)
6. Rhyming slang: 'Up the stairs, apples and ____s' (4)
9. Letters sent and received (4)
10. Jump over (4)
11. Show off (5)
13. Uncooked (3)
15. Rodent that resembles a large mouse (3)

CROSSWORD 109

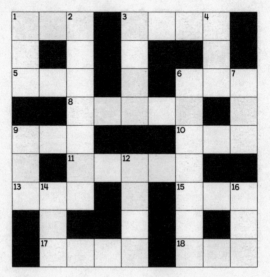

Across

1. Observed (3)
3. Sideways-walking shellfish with pincers and legs (4)
5. Sick; not well (3)
6. Label attached to a present (3)
8. Large, stringed instrument (5)
9. A pair (3)
10. Tall, rounded vase (3)
11. An army officer of high rank (5)
13. Have an obligation to repay something (3)
15. What comes out of a pen (3)
17. Shout loudly (4)
18. Something a child plays with (3)

Down

1. Narrow runner for use on snow (3)
2. Kind greeting on arrival (7)
3. Contact by telephone (4)
4. Sound made by a sheep (3)
6. Someone who visits places abroad (7)
7. Weapon that fires bullets (3)
9. Also; as well (3)
12. Prison (4)
14. How something is done (3)
16. Shaped metal used to unlock a door (3)

CROSSWORD 110

Across

4. Make someone unhappy (5)
6. A young deer (4)
7. Shed tears (3)
9. Someone who lives in Israel (7)
10. Having lived for a long time (3)
12. Skin of a fruit or vegetable (4)
13. Quarrel; disagree (5)

Down

1. Famished (6)
2. Abbreviation for a sixtieth of a minute (3)
3. Flavouring for sweet food (7)
5. Sports shoe with rubber sole (7)
8. Often accompanies salt on a table (6)
11. Remove moisture from an item of clothing (3)

CROSSWORD 111

Across

1. Walk like a soldier (5)
4. Metal container (3)
6. Model of a person used to scare birds away from crops (9)
7. Time between morning and evening (9)
10. Waterproof coat (3)
11. Something very unusual, such as 'a _____ storm' (5)

Down

1. If you muddle something or make it dirty then you make a ____ (4)
2. To do with love (8)
3. Rabbit-like, fast-running animal (4)
4. Slow creature with a shell (8)
5. At this time (3)
7. Point at a target (3)
8. Covering on a house (4)
9. The unusually long part of a giraffe's body (4)

CROSSWORD 112

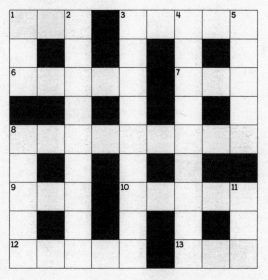

Across

1. Drink slowly (3)
3. Snack food often served with hamburgers (5)
6. Sight, hearing, touch, taste or smell (5)
7. Evening before an important day (3)
8. Roman who fought in public displays (9)
9. Old-age pensioner (inits) (3)
10. Sticky (5)
12. A person who is against you (5)
13. Fleshy edge of the mouth (3)

Down

1. Urgent call for help (inits) (3)
2. Large, tropical fruit with prickly skin (9)
3. Science subject (9)
4. Exactly the same (9)
5. Use rude words (5)
8. Ball-shaped map of the Earth (5)
11. Small barking sound (3)

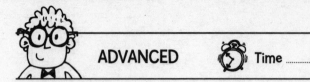
CROSSWORD 113

Across

1. Picture made by sticking together scraps of paper (7)
6. Pester or repeatedly complain to someone (3)
7. You might have rashers of this at breakfast (5)
8. Moving staircase (9)
10. Strong claw, often found on a bird (5)
12. A joke based on multiple meanings of words (3)
13. Thick, sticky liquid made from sugar (7)

Down

1. Bits of coloured paper thrown at a wedding (8)
2. Correct thinking (5)
3. Vehicle for carrying injured people to hospital (9)
4. Short for et cetera; 'and other things like this' (3)
5. The way in to a place (8)
9. Subject (5)
11. What the umpire says when they replay a point in tennis (3)

CROSSWORD 114

Across

1. An event, such as a play, that takes place in front of people (11)
7. Bumper car (6)
8. Great anger (4)
9. Woman with magical powers (5)
11. Plant with red flowers, often associated with peace after war (5)
13. Joint connecting your leg to your foot (5)
14. Bread that has gone hard is _____ (5)
16. Not costing anything (4)
18. Pass on an illness to someone else (6)
20. The act of drawing a line underneath a word (11)

Down

2. A feeling (7)
3. Soft, pear-shaped fruit with many small seeds (3)
4. Slope (4)
5. Place where planes take off and land (7)
6. Wheel with teeth used in mechanisms (3)
10. School for continuing education (7)
12. Large bird with pouch in beak for holding fish (7)
15. Used for keeping money in a shop (4)
17. *Harry Potter* character, Weasley (3)
19. Part of a fish, used to help with swimming (3)

ACE PUZZLER

CROSSWORD 115

Across

1. Opening in a wall, usually filled with glass (6)
3. Grated peel of a lemon or orange (4)
5. Juicy fruit, like a small peach (7)
7. Metal fastening (3)
8. Shown where to go (3)
10. Large country house, especially in Roman times (5)
11. Small, poisonous snake (5)
12. Opposite of good (3)
14. Part of the body between the feet and the hips (3)
16. Mix playing cards together (7)
18. Piece of music (4)
19. Sitting room (6)

Down

1. Cry (4)
2. The colour of milk (5)
3. Place where wild animals are kept for people to see (3)
4. Someone who makes fitted coats and trousers (6)
5. The horns on a deer (7)
6. Young frog without legs (7)
8. Scientist's workplace (3)
9. Disc with a film or TV show on it (inits) (3)
10. Small plant with purple flowers (6)
13. Really terrible (5)
15. Substance used for sticking things together (4)
17. Tint; colour (3)

CROSSWORD 116

Across

1. Four-way junction in the road (10)
5. Desert animal with one or two humps and long eyelashes (5)
7. Hook-shaped Christmas sweet, _ _ _ _ _ cane (5)
9. Too much (6)
10. Easy to break (4)
12. Secret plan to do something bad (4)
13. Crispy Indian pastry case filled with meat or vegetables (6)
16. To walk heavily (5)
17. Party where people dance (5)
18. One-hundredth of a metre (10)

Down

1. Ride on a bicycle (5)
2. If you jump into a swimming pool, you will make a _ _ _ _ _ _ (6)
3. Cry of pain (4)
4. Not safe (9)
6. Device used for reheating food (9)
8. Long-haired ox (3)
11. Bicycle for two people (6)
12. Container for flowers (3)
14. On your own; by yourself (5)
15. Pimple (4)

CROSSWORD 117

Across

1. A place with a telescope for looking at the stars (11)
6. Large, edible fish with pink flesh (6)
7. A small island (4)
8. How fast something moves (5)
11. Map book (5)
12. The rotation between two lines, measured in degrees (5)
13. Chipped potatoes (5)
17. Round lump, for example on a camel's back (4)
18. Burning brightly (6)
19. Clever; brainy (11)

Down

1. Green place in the middle of a desert (5)
2. Work out a solution (5)
3. Plant on which grapes grow (4)
4. Bird chirping noise (7)
5. Let go; set free (7)
9. Black and white, flightless seabird (7)
10. Shadow of the Earth on the moon (7)
14. Picture (5)
15. Tasting like sugar (5)
16. When the dog was happy, he would wag his ____ (4)

CROSSWORD 118

Across

7. A minor actor who doesn't usually speak (5)
8. For example, Black Beauty (5)
9. Curved arch of colours (7)
10. Male child (3)
11. Item of clothing for women (5)
13. Instructions you must obey (5)
15. Text-speak laugh (inits) (3)
17. Scary creature (7)
20. Red, green or yellow fruit with hard skin and a crunchy middle (5)
21. Bright spring flower that grows from a bulb (5)

Down

1. Forest grazing animal with hooves (4)
2. An organized refusal to work (6)
3. Young sheep (4)
4. Wash your body under falling water (6)
5. Coloured part of the eye (4)
6. Wimbledon sport (6)
11. US currency unit (6)
12. Season between spring and winter (6)
14. Small (6)
16. Two of these at the entrance to your mouth (4)
18. Short message or letter (4)
19. Thick string (4)

ACE PUZZLER

CROSSWORD 119

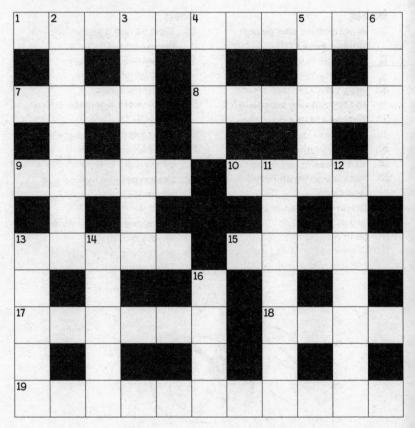

Across

1. An interesting change in a story or events (11)
7. Shout this to appeal for assistance (4)
8. Long cake filled with cream and topped with chocolate (6)
9. Place where milk is processed (5)
10. Incorrect; untrue (5)
13. Very alert (5)
15. Spicy Indian sauce-based food (5)
17. Colour made by mixing red and yellow (6)
18. Long walk (4)
19. What flows in wires to power TVs and other devices (11)

Down

2. Short hair on your eyelid (7)
3. For example, Caesar or Augustus (7)
4. Allow access to (4)
5. Electronic mail (5)
6. Number of corners on a triangle (5)
11. Living in water (7)
12. Snake (7)
13. Make loud noises while you sleep (5)
14. Not asleep (5)
16. Drop of water from your eye (4)

ACE PUZZLER

CROSSWORD 120

Across

3. The day before tomorrow (5)
6. An Italian meal made from rice (7)
7. Unpleasant; horrible (5)
8. Hard cereal seed, such as wheat (5)
9. Slice with a knife (3)
11. Grumble (5)
13. A mistake (5)
15. Tropical vegetable, like a potato (3)
18. Dish for eating from (5)
19. Wide (5)
20. Against the law (7)
21. Colour for 'go' (5)

Down

1. Look in this to see yourself (6)
2. Vacation (7)
3. You lick ice cream with this (6)
4. Clean; remove dirt from (4)
5. Toy that goes up and down on a string (2,2)
10. Cart or wheeled basket used for shopping (7)
12. Serviette (6)
14. Robber; bandit (6)
16. Male deer (4)
17. Wicked behaviour (4)

ACE PUZZLER

CROSSWORD 121

Across

1. Woman (4)
4. Write your signature (4)
7. Wonder (3)
9. Joint of your arm (5)
10. Shut something (5)
11. Currency used in many European countries (4)
12. Put in (6)
14. Response to a question (6)
16. Place where pigs and cows are often kept (4)
19. Woolly animal, similar to a small camel without a hump (5)
20. Liquid unit (5)
21. Abbreviation for the day after Wednesday (3)
22. Primary colour (4)
23. Many people buy cats to catch ____ (4)

Down

2. A yellow colour; a resin used in jewellery (5)
3. Deep breath when you are tired (4)
4. There are sixty in a minute (6)
5. Small person made of clay and placed in the garden (5)
6. Plant used for food (9)
8. Ninth month (9)
13. Discuss (6)
15. Small garden creature that leaves a shiny trail (5)
17. Room under the roof of a house (5)
18. Unhappy (4)

ACE PUZZLER

CROSSWORD 122

Across

1. A folding chair that you might take to the beach (9)
7. Round vegetable with strong smell (5)
8. Symbol used to indicate subtraction (5)
10. After the expected time (4)
11. Colourful part of a plant (6)
14. Attractive; nice to look at (6)
15. Large African wildcat with a shaggy mane (4)
17. Someone who flies a plane (5)
19. Plenty; more than enough (5)
20. An exciting journey or event (9)

Down

2. Biblical letter (7)
3. For example, Henry VIII (4)
4. Modest (6)
5. A small hotel (3)
6. Hard candy on a stick (8)
9. Someone you don't know (8)
12. Speak softly (7)
13. Carved model of a person or animal (6)
16. Feel you would like something, as in 'I ____ this' (4)
18. Cover for a jar (3)

ACE PUZZLER

CROSSWORD 123

Across

1. Close to but not necessarily the same as (11)
7. Photo-taking device (6)
8. Deep breath of relief or sadness (4)
9. A room used for writing (5)
11. Instruction to a dog to go and get something (5)
13. You do this to show that you're happy (5)
14. Wild, wolf-like animal with wicked laugh (5)
16. A walking track (4)
18. Counting tool with sliding beads (6)
20. Either of your parents' fathers (11)

Down

2. Ghost (7)
3. Fish eggs (3)
4. Photograph taken of the inside of the body (1,3)
5. Something strange or unexplained (7)
6. Hard pull (3)
10. Friendly sea animal with a fin (7)
12. Perform a magic trick (7)
15. A young cow (4)
17. What we breathe (3)
19. Appropriate; suitable (3)

ACE PUZZLER

CROSSWORD 124

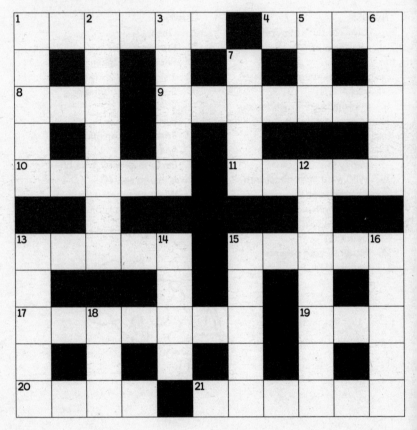

Across

1. Private piece of information (6)
4. You might ask a hairdresser for this (4)
8. Belonging to us (3)
9. To show or display in a museum (7)
10. Stomach (5)
11. Device for measuring time, worn on the wrist (5)
13. Healthy mix of cold, raw vegetables (5)
15. Not a lie (5)
17. Invisible line marking halfway between the North and South Poles (7)
19. Wild animal's home (3)
20. Hold on to (4)
21. Small, dark red fruit on a stalk with a stone in the centre (6)

Down

1. The opposite of long (5)
2. Soft toffee (7)
3. All of a group (5)
5. What Aladdin did to the lamp (3)
6. Football game (5)
7. Melt from frozen (4)
12. Noise that accompanies lightning (7)
13. Say words (5)
14. Appointment (4)
15. Portable light (5)
16. Food product made by bees (5)
18. Utilize something (3)

ACE PUZZLER

CROSSWORD 125

Across

1. Swelling (4)
4. Desire (4)
7. Choose something (3)
8. If you visit the US you are going to ___ (7)
10. Season between winter and summer (6)
12. Glass part of spectacles (4)
13. Something by which a person or place is called (4)
15. The _____ Dodger, a character in *Oliver Twist* (6)
19. Great joy (7)
20. Perform on stage (3)
21. A steady pain (4)
22. Find appealing (4)

Down

2. Say something clearly (5)
3. Shellfish, like a large shrimp (5)
4. From Monday to Sunday (4)
5. What the sun does (5)
6. Rubbish (8)
9. Total; complete (8)
11. Frozen water (3)
12. Large number (3)
14. Enjoyable sounds made by instruments or voices (5)
16. To do with kings and queens (5)
17. Camping cup for keeping drinks hot or cold (5)
18. Alike (4)

CROSSWORD 126

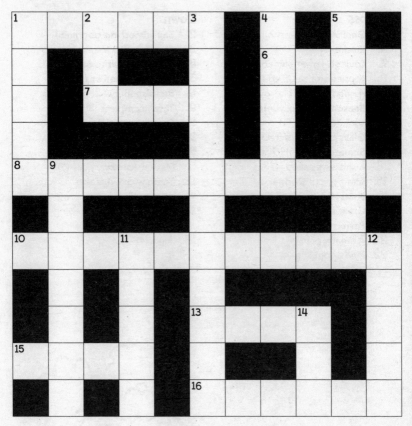

Across

1. On a ship or plane (6)
6. Kind; sort (4)
7. Lovingly touch someone with your lips (4)
8. If I don't waste energy then I am caring for the _____ (11)
10. A TV show which follows real-life events (11)
13. A short measure of length; sneak or creep (4)
15. Breakfast, lunch or dinner, for example (4)
16. Small, useful device or tool (6)

Down

1. Think the same as someone else (5)
2. Large tree with acorns (3)
3. Finding something out (11)
4. Bad weather with thunder and lightning (5)
5. Tool used to tighten bolts (7)
9. Thin pasta strips used in Oriental food (7)
11. Parent's brother (5)
12. Medium-sized sailing boat (5)
14. Clasp tightly (3)

ACE PUZZLER

CROSSWORD 127

Across

7. Large country house with grounds (5)
8. Sound made by a horse (5)
9. Dark green, leafy vegetable (7)
10. Not me, but ___ (3)
11. What you do at night (5)
13. Opposite of smooth (5)
15. Go bad; decay (3)
17. Make food go down your throat (7)
20. Sharp cutting tool (5)
21. Clothing for your feet (5)

Down

1. December 25th (4)
2. Something that powers a vehicle (6)
3. A measurement that's equal to the width times the length (4)
4. Used to stop a boat from moving (6)
5. Really small (4)
6. A common songbird (6)
11. To move your hand gently over a dog or cat (6)
12. Crayon-like colouring stick (6)
14. Open a door with a key (6)
16. Opposite of fat (4)
18. This as well; too (4)
19. Direction in which the sun sets (4)

CROSSWORD 128

Across

1. Cereal plant used for food (4)
4. A pack of playing cards (4)
7. That woman or girl's (3)
9. Deep spoon with long handle, often used to serve soup (5)
10. Music and sound (5)
11. Painful (4)
12. Something that you keep drink in (6)
14. Frail; weak from illness (6)
16. Travel through water using your hands and feet (4)
19. Warning sound (5)
20. Greeting word (5)
21. Pastry dish filled with meat or fruit (3)
22. Insect that destroys crops (4)
23. Make lots of small bubbles (4)

Down

2. Small, poisonous snake (5)
3. Hut for storing gardening tools (4)
4. Mythical winged serpent (6)
5. Young army or police trainee (5)
6. To do with the Greek or Roman world (9)
8. Holiday for a newly married couple (9)
13. Remind someone what to say (6)
15. Tongue of fire (5)
17. A type of formal ballroom dance (5)
18. Someone who cooks your food (4)

ACE PUZZLER

CROSSWORD 129

Across

3. Before second and third (5)
6. Large, African ape (7)
7. Noise made by a cat (5)
8. Fourth month (5)
9. Small drinking mug (3)
11. Bitter, yellow fruit (5)
13. Ketchup is tomato _ _ _ _ _ (5)
15. A long, thin stick, such as one used for fishing (3)
18. A type of canoe (5)
19. House made of ice (5)
20. Loving; loyal (7)
21. With nothing inside (5)

Down

1. Join railway carriages together (6)
2. Someone who stays at a place for a short time (7)
3. Very well known, such as a celebrity (6)
4. Back part of something (4)
5. Place with houses, shops, offices and buildings (4)
10. Light umbrella used in the sunshine (7)
12. Not anyone (6)
14. Mouth of a volcano (6)
16. Flat surface (4)
17. Turn over a pancake (4)

ACE PUZZLER

CROSSWORD 130

Across

1. A black, erasable surface that is written on with chalk (10)
7. Black-and-white bird (6)
8. Used to describe gentle pets (4)
9. Spirit or apparition (5)
11. Find out how heavy something is (5)
13. Thick milk, sometimes added to coffee (5)
14. Common; ordinary (5)
16. Bad or wicked (4)
18. Area around the North Pole (6)
20. Daily publications that report the latest happenings (10)

Down

2. Strong material made from animal skin (7)
3. Soft, flat hat (3)
4. Cow's meat (4)
5. Woman in a play (7)
6. Not very intelligent (3)
10. The opposite of deep (7)
12. Slow-moving mass of ice (7)
15. Illuminates a room (4)
17. A vehicle bigger than a car and suitable for moving things (3)
19. Slang term for a police officer (3)

CROSSWORD 131

Across

7. Elephants' tusks are made of this (5)
8. Rub out (5)
9. Someone who educates you (7)
10. Stop living (3)
11. Underground parts of a tree (5)
13. Very dark wood (5)
15. Feline animal (3)
17. Useful (7)
20. Keyboard instrument (5)
21. Priest (5)

Down

1. For example, spear____ or pepper____ (4)
2. Vegetable used to make chips (6)
3. Traditional story about gods and heroes (4)
4. Unit for measuring temperature (6)
5. When not at sea you are on ____ (4)
6. Long-stemmed crunchy green vegetable, often eaten raw (6)
11. Instructions for cooking food (6)
12. Where lessons take place (6)
14. Building for business work (6)
16. Device for catching animals (4)
18. Strong emotion of liking someone very much (4)
19. Small, light-brown songbird (4)

ACE PUZZLER

CROSSWORD 132

Across

1. Red fruit, often eaten as a vegetable in salad (6)
4. What a red light on a traffic signal tells you to do (4)
8. Plural of 'man' (3)
9. Sickness (7)
10. You do this when you swallow liquid (5)
11. Furniture with legs and a flat top (5)
13. Cloth used to make jeans (5)
15. Natural disaster involving water (5)
17. Mountain that erupts with molten lava (7)
19. Allow someone to do something (3)
20. Large brass instrument (4)
21. Rough drawing (6)

Down

1. Nervous; easily frightened (5)
2. Grand house (7)
3. Deceive someone (5)
5. Abbreviation for the day after Monday (3)
6. Thick glue used for crafts (5)
7. Apartment (4)
12. Small book with paper covers (7)
13. A thick bed covering which you usually put a cover over before using (5)
14. What vegetarians won't eat (4)
15. Dress (5)
16. A dug trench used to carry water (5)
18. Place that scientists work (3)

ACE PUZZLER

CROSSWORD 133

Across

1. Fairly hot (4)
4. Spiders' homes (4)
7. Tool used for chopping wood (3)
9. Paths made for cars (5)
10. A secret spy (5)
11. Something a plant grows from (4)
12. Quick sketch or drawing (6)
14. Knowledge (6)
16. Boat made for travelling at sea (4)
19. Other way to left (5)
20. Make someone smile (5)
21. You say 'these are my ___' when something belongs to you (3)
22. Mix with a spoon (4)
23. Food selected to help someone become healthier (4)

Down

2. Surprise; astonish (5)
3. Decorative face covering (4)
4. An item designed for causing harm (6)
5. Mix together smoothly (5)
6. What you're solving at this very moment (9)
8. Tried (9)
13. Person who looks after the sick (6)
15. Ability to see (5)
17. Building where a family live (5)
18. The palm and fingers (4)

CROSSWORD 134

Across

1. A brightly coloured pen used to colour over important words (11)
7. Soft; not rough (6)
8. Move along on wheels (4)
9. Someone staying in a hotel (5)
11. Shape associated with love (5)
13. What you shed when you cry (5)
14. People who work in an office (5)
16. Raise up; an elevator (4)
18. Regard someone with respect (6)
20. Groups with the power to make decisions (11)

Down

2. Frozen water for putting in a drink (3,4)
3. Covering for the head (3)
4. Thought (4)
5. The gathering of crops (7)
6. Snake-shaped fish (3)
10. Pull something until it gets longer (7)
12. Official at a football match (7)
15. Being just and right (4)
17. A three-letter abbreviation for 'I owe you' (inits) (3)
19. The cat sat on the ___ (3)

ACE PUZZLER

CROSSWORD 135

Across

1. Make sense of something (10)
7. Also (2,4)
8. Handle a situation successfully (4)
9. Newly made (5)
11. Sandy seashore (5)
13. Woven fabric (5)
14. Remains of a tree after it has been cut down (5)
16. Solemn promise (4)
18. Night-time cushion (6)
20. A flying vehicle with a rotor on top (10)

Down

2. Nose opening (7)
3. Preceding day (3)
4. Often goes with pepper (4)
5. From a time long ago (7)
6. Quick swim (3)
10. Type of school bag (7)
12. Write music (7)
15. A long story, such as *The Odyssey* (4)
17. The blackened remains of a fire (3)
19. Body part for resting a computer (3)

CROSSWORD 136

Across

3. Overtake (4)
5. A small piece of rock (5)
6. Printed words (4)
8. Car with driver available for hire (4)
10. Question someone (3)
11. Repeatedly hit the palms of your hands together (4)
13. Fasten a door to prevent entry (4)
15. Period of time during sunlight (3)
17. Strange; unusual (3)
19. Repair (4)
21. Small, jumping insect (4)
22. Enjoyment (3)
23. Large, hairy monster that's said to live in the Himalayan mountains (4)
25. Reflection of sound (4)
26. Christmas hymn (5)
27. A red jewel (4)

Down

1. An area of land that is entirely surrounded by water (6)
2. Banana-eating animal (6)
3. Animal kept at home (3)
4. To glue something to something else (5)
7. Point of a pencil (3)
9. In the past (3)
12. Help (3)
13. Tell a fib (3)
14. Large edible sea fish, often served with chips (3)
16. The whole quantity of something (3)
17. British city famous for its very old university (6)
18. Hang or swing loosely (6)
19. Person in charge of a town council (5)
20. Something you use to catch fish (3)
21. Payment; charge (3)
24. Very cold (3)

ACE PUZZLER

CROSSWORD 137

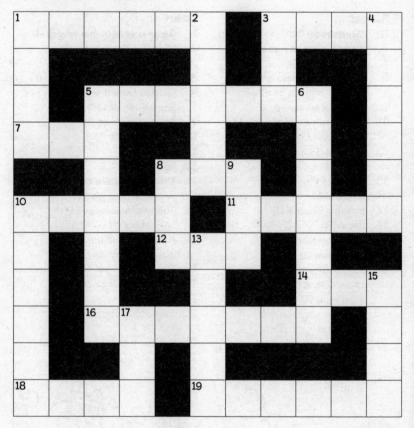

Across
1. Packed meal that you eat outside, such as in the park (6)
3. Law (4)
5. A four-sided shape with two different lengths of side (7)
7. A single item (3)
8. Prompt to turn over (inits) (3)
10. The Queen's favourite dog (5)
11. Left over; not used (5)
12. A particular item, as in 'I want ___ one over there' (3)
14. Not cooked (3)
16. Brass instrument (7)
18. Tiny pieces of rock found on beaches (4)
19. Metal spike used for sewing (6)

Down
1. Game played on horseback (4)
2. Object in sky with bright tail (5)
3. Flow, like water from a tap (3)
4. Group of countries ruled by one person or country (6)
5. Remove ice from something (7)
6. Pudding (7)
8. Large hole (3)
9. Have a need to pay something back (3)
10. Colourful spring flower that grows from a bulb (6)
13. A person, as distinguished from other animals (5)
15. Walk through shallow water (4)
17. Primary painting colour (3)

ACE PUZZLER

CROSSWORD 138

Across

3. Pale (5)
6. Singing along and following words on a screen (7)
7. Copy a picture by drawing over it on thin paper (5)
8. Green or purple fruit that grows on vines (5)
9. Abbreviation for the final month of the year, as you might see on a calendar (3)
11. Very small person (5)
13. Answer (5)
15. Make a mistake (3)
18. Raised platform for theatre shows (5)
19. To stay in bed in the morning (3,2)
20. A flow of water in a river or the sea (7)
21. A young person (5)

Down

1. Opposite of wide (6)
2. Blood-sucking monster (7)
3. A, B or C (6)
4. Horned farmyard animal (4)
5. An oak, a sycamore or a fir, for example (4)
10. A score of 100 in cricket (7)
12. From France (6)
14. An old story from the past that may or may not be true (6)
16. Take part in a game (4)
17. List of food options in a restaurant (4)

ACE PUZZLER

CROSSWORD 139

Across

7. Loud sound (5)
8. Beneath (5)
9. Here and now (7)
10. Attempt (3)
11. Furry Australian animal that eats eucalyptus leaves (5)
13. Large stream (5)
15. Male parent (3)
17. Machine for carrying people or goods (7)
20. Nut from an oak tree (5)
21. Small, furry animal with a long tail (5)

Down

1. The sound a stick makes when it breaks (4)
2. Place to see a film (6)
3. At this place (4)
4. Spread made by churning milk (6)
5. Change (4)
6. Words said when praying (6)
11. Capture by force (6)
12. The period before Christmas (6)
14. _____ cleaner, used for hoovering (6)
16. Building entrance (4)
18. Place where a person lives (4)
19. Level (4)

ALL THE
ANSWERS

1

6

11

2

7

12

3

8

13

4

9

14

5

10

15

16

	S	H	O	P
	E		O	
T	R	A	M	P
R		R		
Y	E	T	I	

21

R	U	S	H	
A		H		W
F	L	A	M	E
T		P		E
	W	E	A	K

17

L	O	B		A
E		R	U	B
A		E		B
S	E	A		E
H		D	A	Y

22

L	A	P		P
O		A	L	L
B		S		A
B	A	T		T
Y		A	G	E

18

G		A		D
U	N	D	E	R
A		U		E
R	O	L	L	S
D		T		S

23

O		S		J
N	O	I	S	E
I		R		A
O	C	E	A	N
N		N		S

19

	T		K	
V	I	C	A	R
	M	A	Y	
V	I	T	A	L
	D		K	

24

	N		L	
C	A	R	O	L
	K	E	Y	
M	E	D	A	L
	D		L	

20

	R	U	B	Y
	O		L	
I	D	E	A	L
	E		C	
L	O	C	K	

25
```
  S   D U C K
T A X I   O
  U   A   M
  S U M U P
  A   O   O
  G   N E S T
M E N D   E
```

30
```
  W I S D O M
  O   O   A
P R E S E N T
  R     A
E Y E L A S H
  A   I   T
T R O P H Y
```

35
```
  A   T   I
E M E R A L D
  E   A   L
C R A C K E R
  I   T   G
A C R O B A T
  A   R   L
```

26
```
N O B O D Y
I   R   E
B L O S S O M
    T   S
A T H L E T E
    E   R   R
  C R A T E R
```

31
```
    E V A D E
  N   E   O
F A S H I O N
  R   I   D
F R E C K L E
  O   L   E
S W E E P
```

36
```
C O A S T
R   N   O W N
I   C A R   A
S K I   N I P
P   E R A   K
S O N   D   I
    T H O R N
```

27
```
  M     K
  L E T T E R
W I N     N
  Q U E E N
  U     V E T
T I N S E L
  D     N
```

32
```
O G R E
  A   C U T
  L   L   E
P A T I E N T
  X   P   N
  Y E S   I
      E A S T
```

37
```
F A S T
R   E   G O D
E X C E L   E
N   O   O   G
C   N E V E R
H A D   E   E
    I S L E
```

28
```
    V
  C H I P S
  L   S   N
H O L I D A Y
  C   T   C
  K N O C K
      R
```

33
```
      C
  F R U I T
  L   R   R
D O O R M A T
  O   A   C
  D A N C E
      T
```

38
```
T H R E E
R   A   V I P
A L I V E   O
V   N   N   W
E   B L I N D
L O O   N   E
    W A G E R
```

29
```
  P R I S O N
  T     W   E
S O L V E   I
K   E   A   G
I   M A R C H
R   O     U
T O N G U E
```

34
```
G U I T A R
U   C   C
T H E A T R E
    C   R
S T U D E N T
    B   S
  S E A S O N
```

39
```
  F     L
  P I C N I C
P A L   T
  S M A R T
  T   O L D
B E E T L E
  L     L
```

40

```
S A M O S A
A   I   E
D E S T R O Y
    T   I
F L A V O U R
    K   U   A
  P E R S O N
```

45

```
    S I G H T
P A W   L   U
U   A L I E N
P   L   T   N
P I L O T   E
E   O   E E L
T O W E R
```

50

```
  R   G   S
V I L L A I N
  S   A   L
T O A S T E R
  T   S   N
S T R E T C H
  O   S   E
```

41

```
  C   T A L L
S O U R   E
  N   A   T
J O I N T   E
  U   N   E
  R   E A R L
Y E A R   S
```

46

```
A S S I S T
P   H   A
E Q U A T O R
    T   C
K E T C H U P
    L   E   E
  Y E L L O W
```

51

```
T O P I C
O   R   O F F
F L O A T   I
F   J   T   L
E   E M A I L
E T C   G   E
    T R E A T
```

42

```
  R   O   W
T E A C H E R
  L   T   L
C A G O U L E
  T   B   I
R E F E R E E
  D   R   S
```

47

```
O A S I S
R   U   A T E
A P R O N   N
N   N   D   A
G   A L A R M
E L M   L   E
  E A S E L
```
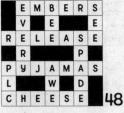

52

```
I N V I T E
M   A   O
P E N G U I N
  I   R
S O L D I E R
  L   S   A
L A P T O P
```

43

```
A M P L E
B   R   M A C
S C O O P   E
O   B   E   R
R   L A R G E
B Y E   O   A
  M U R A L
```

48

```
  E M B E R S
  V   E   E
R E L E A S E
  R       P
P Y J A M A S
L   W   D
C H E E S E
```

53

```
  A M U S E
  B   O   E
M O R N I N G
  T   S   I
S T A T I O N
  L   E   R
B E A R D
```

44

```
A T T I C
S   H   O A P
T   U R N   E
H E N   C O P
M   D U E   P
A G E   A   E
  R U L E R
```

49

```
  S     C
  J I G S A W
W A G   M
  G N O M E
U   O R E
B A N A N A
  R     K
```

55
```
. D W A R F
S H E . B . A
Y . F E A S T
M . R . N . H
B L O O D . E
O . S . O A R
L A T I N
```

60
```
T A S K
I . P . S I P
P E R C H . I
T . I . I . L
O . N O V E L
E G G . E . O
. . . C R O W
```

65
```
. H . T . V
J O U R N A L
. R . E . L
A I R M A I L
. Z . B . A
G O S L I N G
. N . E . T
```

56
```
T O T A L
I . R . E V E
C R U S T . X
K . M . T . P
E . P A U S E
T I E . C . R
. . T H E F T
```

61
```
. S . S I C K
D E E P . A .
. R . I . L .
. P A N I C .
. E . A . I .
. N . C L U B
I T C H . M .
```

66
```
G I R L S
. Y . E . P E R
M E D I A . E .
K . U . N . M .
I . C A N O E .
T U E . E . D .
. D I R T Y
```

57
```
. . C
. T R O U T
. O . M . O
V A M P I R E
. S . L . C
. T E E T H
. . . X
```

62
```
. . P
. B L O O M
. E . S . E
P A T T E R N
. C . M . C
. H E A V Y
. . . N
```

58
```
O A T H
. U . A I M
. G . N . A
P U D D I N G
. S . B . G
. T E A . E
. . G I R L
```

63
```
. . E A G L E
B O X . A . X
R . C E L L O
I . L . L . T
G R A P E . I
H . I . R A C
T U M M Y
```

59
```
. S W O R D
. V . E . E
C O L L E C T
. L . C . I
R U D O L P H
. M . M . E
J E W E L
```

64
```
R A I S I N
U . S . L
G O R I L L A
. A . N
P R E T E N D
. L . S . I
. T I S S U E
```

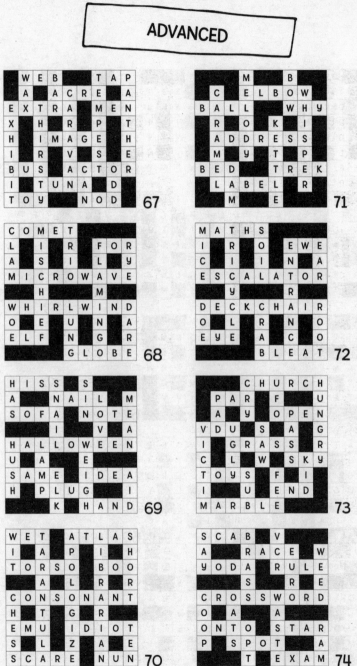

Puzzle 75

```
. . A . H . .
. T L O G I C
W O R M . S E T
. D O . R . N
. D E N T I S T
. L . D B . U
N E T . B A R K
. R A D I O . Y
. G . . N
```

75

Puzzle 76

```
W I P E R
E . E . O . V A T
B . E . O . A . E
S C R A M B L E D
. . A . . U
N I G H T M A R E
A . E . I . B . V
G A S . C . L . I
. . . K N E E L
```

76

Puzzle 77

```
F E W . O U T
A . R A W . H . S
T W O . L I E I N
. . N . . N . U
L I G H T N I N G
A . U . G . L
M A N G O . L I T
B . E . A G O . O
. W O K . O N E
```

77

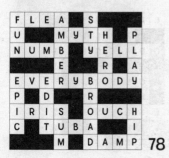

Puzzle 78

```
F L E A . S
U . M Y T H . P
N U M B . Y E L L
. . E . R . A
E V E R Y B O D Y
P . D . R
I R I S . O U C H
C . T U B A . I
. M . D A M P
```

78

Puzzle 79

```
. . S . D .
. P . C H E A T
F A I R . D R Y
. R . E G . O
. S P E C I A L
. N . N G . L
B I G . . G L E E
. P E T A L . Y
. L . . E
```

79

Puzzle 80

```
D Y E . S O A P
E . C . L . . E
W A S . O . F A N
. . T O W E L . I
V I A . . O I L
O . S T R A W
W A Y . A . E B B
. R . I . R . U
M O O N . S A G
```

80

Puzzle 81

```
S L E E P
A . L . O . D I P
V . E . L . I . I
E S P I O N A G E
. . H . . L
T O A D S T O O L
O . N . T . G . U
P A T . A . U . C
. . G R E E K
```

81

Puzzle 82

```
D O M I N O E S
O . A . . U . U
G U Y . F R I E S
. . O . R . . H
H O R S E S H O E
U . . S . E
B E N C H . L A W
. I . O . L . A
D O W N P O U R
```

82

83

- A · M
- L · BLUES
- FOUR · THU
- B · O · P · A
- SEAGULL · L
- T · D · R · L
- FED · PLOT
- ROYAL · W
- T · E

87

- M · A
- J · AWARD
- FANG · TIP
- N · P · T · A
- UNIFORM
- A · E · M · O
- ERR · AUNT
- YACHT · D
- N · O

84

- DEC · FARM
- I · O · I · O
- GYM · Z · WON
- PIZZA · O
- TOO · ROW
- O · SUGAR
- NUT · O · ICY
- S · A · O · A
- EXIT · RIP

88

- OSTRICH
- V · R · M · A · P
- ERA · PASTA · A
- R · I · A · V
- CONSTABLE
- A · I · L · M
- STONE · AGE
- T · A · N · D · N
- PATIENT

85

- CADET
- HE · I · R · PAY
- E · N · A · R · E
- FOOTPRINT
- S · N
- CLASSICAL
- O · U · T · E · I
- TAR · O · S · V
- PASTE

89

- DISTRESS
- A · M · E · O
- BAA · GLASS
- L · E · E
- VALENTINE
- I · I · D
- PEACE · EAT
- M · U · A · E
- UMBRELLA

86

- RABBIT
- FLU · U · U
- L · N · STIR · R
- BYE · T · R · K
- A · CORGI · E
- L · H · Y · MAY
- LION · H · P
- E · A · OWE
- TEMPLE

90

- LIPS · PICK
- E · E · L · U
- O · SATCHEL · L
- PTO · A · E · E
- A · COBRA · T
- R · K · L · RUT
- DESSERT · E
- V · U · A · R
- MEAN · PLUS

91

```
I  V  O  R  Y
D  I  O     S  I  P
E  N  Y     H  E
A  S  T  R  O  N  A  U  T
   M        M
T  R  E  A  T  M  E  N  T
O  N     U     F     I
W  E  T     N     U     N
      A  L  L  E  Y
```

95

```
K  I  S  S     F  O  O  D
E     U     O     W
T     E  M  E  R  A  L  D
C  A  R     V     G     E
H     A  M  A  Z  E     F
U     S     D     N  O  R
P  R  E  S  E  N  T     O
   A     K     U     S
U  G  L  Y     N  E  S  T
```

92

```
S  T  U  D  E  N  T
C     N     N     U     O
O  D  D     T  I  G  E  R
R     E     E           I
P  A  R  T  R  I  D  G  E
I           T     A     N
O  P  E  R  A     N  E  T
N     T     I     C     A
   C  O  N  C  E  A  L
```

96

```
V  O  W  E  L
E     A     A     O  F  F
S     R     D     V     A
T  E  D  D  Y  B  E  A  R
      R           R
P  R  O  F  E  S  S  O  R
A     B     X     E     U
L  I  E     A     A     B
      M  E  S  S  Y
```

93

```
S  N  O  W     Y
I        A  R  E  A     I
T  E  S  T     S  C  A  R
      E        R     O
E  V  E  R  G  R  E  E  N
A     A     E
R  U  S  H     P  U  R  E
L     T  A  I  L     L
      D     Y  O  L  K
```

97

```
      U     G
   U     S  H  E  E  T
K  N  E  E     L  O  B
   I     F     T     R
   C  A  U  T  I  O  N
   O     L     N     A
A  R  M     S  I  D  E
N  U  R  S  E     O
   G     L
```

94

```
      C  L  U  B
F     L  O  L     O
R  Y  E     A     P  O  P
E     T  O  W  E  R     O
N  O  T        A  L  L
C     E  M  P  T  Y     L
H  E  R     U     E  Y  E
   L     S  I  R     N
   F  I  S  H
```

98

```
B  A  S  E  B  A  L  L
A     M     S     I
T  I  E     P  H  O  T  O
      L     A     A
V  O  L  U  N  T  E  E  R
I        D     A
A  R  E  N  A     G  A  G
   A     I     L     A
M  A  T  T  R  E  S  S
```

99

103

100

104

101

105

102

106

```
H O L L Y . .
I . A . O . M E T
I S . N . G O . H
S I G N A T U R E
. . U . . . N . .
S P A G H E T T I
A . G . O . A . T
D U E . O . I . C
. . . T E N T H .
```
107

```
M A R C H . . . .
E . O . A . T I N
S . M . R . O . O
S C A R E C R O W
. . N . . . T . .
A F T E R N O O N
I . I . O . I . E
M A C . O . S . C
. . . F R E A K .
```
111

```
J A Z Z . P . . .
I . E X I T . P .
G R A B . T R U E
. . R . . E . A .
P O L A R B E A R
O . E . O . . . .
S T A R . A J A R
T . P A S S . . A
. . W . T E X T .
```
108

```
S I P . C H I P S
O . I . H . D . W
S E N S E . E V E
. . E . M . N . A
G L A D I A T O R
L . P . S . I . .
O A P . T A C K Y
B . L . R . A . A
E N E M Y . L I P
```
112

```
S A W . C R A B .
K . E . A . . A .
I L L . L . T A G
. . C E L L O . U
T W O . . . U R N
O . M A J O R . .
O W E . A . I N K
. A . . I . S . E
. Y E L L . T O Y
```
109

```
. . H . D . . .
. V . U P S E T
F A W N . . C R Y
. N . G . P . A
. I S R A E L I
. L . Y . P . N
O L D . . P E E L
. A R G U E . R
. . Y . . . R .
```
110

```
C O L L A G E . .
O . O . M . T . E
N A G . B A C O N
F . I . U . . . T
E S C A L A T O R
T . . A . O . . A
T A L O N . P U N
I . E . C . I . C
. T R E A C L E .
```
113

ACE PUZZLER

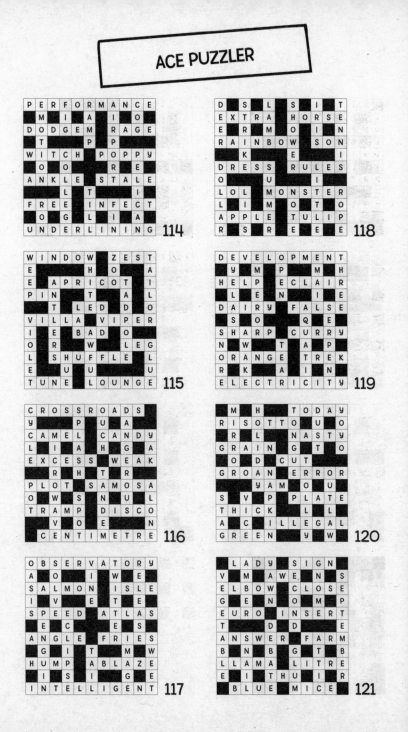

114

```
P E R F O R M A N C E
  M   I   A   I   O
D O D G E M   R A G E
  T   P   P   P
W I T C H   P O P P Y
  O   O   O   R   E
A N K L E   S T A L E
  L   T       I
F R E E   I N F E C T
  O   G   L   I   A
U N D E R L I N I N G
```

118

```
D   S   L   S   I   T
E X T R A   H O R S E
E   R   M   O   I   N
R A I N B O W   S O N
  K   E       I
D R E S S   R U L E S
O   U       I
L O L   M O N S T E R
L   I   M   O   T   O
A P P L E   T U L I P
R   S   R   E   E   E
```

115

```
W I N D O W   Z E S T
E   H   O       A
  A P R I C O T   I
P I N   T   A   L O
  N   T   L E D   D   O
V I L L A   V I P E R
I   E   B A D   O
O   R   W   L E G
L   S H U F F L E   L
E   U   U       U
T U N E   L O U N G E
```

119

```
D E V E L O P M E N T
  Y   M   P   M   H
H E L P   E C L A I R
  L   E   N   I   E
D A I R Y   F A L S E
  S   O       Q   E
S H A R P   C U R R Y
N   W   T   A   P
O R A N G E   T R E K
R   K   A   I   N
E L E C T R I C I T Y
```

116

```
C R O S S R O A D S
Y   P   U   A
C A M E L   C A N D Y
L   I   A   H   G   A
E X C E S S   W E A K
  R   H   T   R
P L O T   S A M O S A
O   W   S   N   U   L
T R A M P   D I S C O
  V   O   E       N
  C E N T I M E T R E
```

120

```
  M   H   T O D A Y
R I S O T T O   U   O
  R   L   N A S T Y
G R A I N   G   T   O
  O   D   C U T
G R O A N   E R R O R
  Y A M   O   U
S   V   P   P L A T E
T H I C K   L   L
A   C   I L L E G A L
G R E E N   Y   W
```

117

```
O B S E R V A T O R Y
A   O   I   W   E
S A L M O N   I S L E
I   V   E   T   E
S P E E D   A T L A S
  E   C   E   S
A N G L E   F R I E S
  G   I   T   M   W
H U M P   A B L A Z E
  I   S   I   G   E
I N T E L L I G E N T
```

121

```
  L A D Y   S I G N
V   M   A W E   N   S
E L B O W   C L O S E
G   E   N   O   M   P
E U R O   I N S E R T
T   D   D   E
A N S W E R   F A R M
B   N   B   G   T   B
L L A M A   L I T R E
E   I   T H U   I   R
  B L U E   M I C E
```

122

```
  D E C K C H A I R
L P   I   U   N
O N I O N   M I N U S
L   S   G   B       T
L A T E   F L O W E R
I   L   S   E   H   A
P R E T T Y   L I O N
O       A   W   S   G
P I L O T   A M P L E
    I   U   N   E   R
  A D V E N T U R E
```

126

```
A B O A R D   S   S
G   A     I   T Y P E
R   K I S S   O   A
E         C   R   N
E N V I R O N M E N T
  O       V     E
D O C U M E N T A R Y
  D   N   R       A
  L   C   I N C H   C
M E A L   N     U   H
  S   E   G A D G E T
```

123

```
A P P R O X I M A T E
  H   O   R   U   U
C A M E R A   S I G H
  N       Y   T
S T U D Y   F E T C H
  O   O     R   O
S M I L E   H Y E N A
    P   C       J
P A T H   A B A C U S
  I   I   L   P   R
G R A N D F A T H E R
```

127

```
X   E   A   A   T   T
M A N O R   N E I G H
A   G   E   C   N   R
S P I N A C H   Y O U
  N       O     S
S L E E P   R O U G H
T     A     N
R O T   S W A L L O W
O   H   T   L   O   E
K N I F E   S O C K S
E   N   L   O   K   T
```

124

```
S E C R E T   T R I M
H   A   V   T   U   A
O U R   E X H I B I T
R   A   R   A     C
T U M M Y   W A T C H
    E       H
S A L A D   T R U T H
P     A   O   N   O
E Q U A T O R   D E N
A   S   E   C   E   E
K E E P   C H E R R Y
```

128

```
  O A T S   D E C K
C   D   H E R   A   H
L A D L E   A U D I O
A   E   D   G   E   N
S O R E   B O T T L E
S     P   N       Y
I N F I R M   S W I M
C   L   O   C   A   O
A L A R M   H E L L O
L   M   P I E   T   N
  P E S T   F I Z Z
```

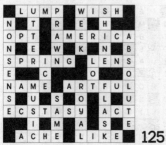

125

```
  L U M P   W I S H
N   T   R   E   H
O P T   A M E R I C A
N   E   W   K   N   B
S P R I N G   L E N S
E   C       O   O
N A M E   A R T F U L
S   U   S   O   L   U
E C S T A S Y   A C T
    I   M   A   S   E
  A C H E   L I K E
```

129

```
  C   V   F I R S T
G O R I L L A   E   O
  U   S   M I A O W
A P R I L   O   R   N
  L   T   C U P
L E M O N   S A U C E
    R O D   R   R
S   F   B   K A Y A K
I G L O O     S   T
D   I   D E V O T E D
E M P T Y     L   R
```

130

```
B L A C K B O A R D
  E   A   E   C   I
M A G P I E   T A M E
  T   F   R
G H O S T   W E I G H
  E   H   S   L
C R E A M   U S U A L
      L   L   C
E V I L   A R C T I C
  A   O   M   O   E
N E W S P A P E R S
```

131

```
M   P   M   D   L   C
I V O R Y   E R A S E
N   T   T   G   N   L
T E A C H E R   D I E
    T   E       R
R O O T S   E B O N Y
E   C       F
C A T   H E L P F U L
I   R   O   O   I   A
P I A N O   V I C A R
E   P   L   E   E   K
```

132

```
T O M A T O   S T O P
I   A   R   F   U   A
M E N   I L L N E S S
I   S   C   A       T
D R I N K   T A B L E
    O           O
D E N I M   F L O O D
U   E   R   K   I
V O L C A N O   L E T
E   A   T   C   E   C
T U B A   S K E T C H
```

133

```
  W A R M   W E B S
C   M   A X E   L   A
R O A D S   A G E N T
O   Z   K   P   N   T
S E E D   D O O D L E
S   D   N       M
W I S D O M   S H I P
O   I   C   H   O   T
R I G H T   A M U S E
D   H   O W N   S   D
  S T I R   D I E T
```

134

```
H I G H L I G H T E R
  C   A   D   A   E
G E N T L E   R O L L
  C   A   V
G U E S T   H E A R T
  B   T   S   E
T E A R S   S T A F F
    E   F   E
L I F T   A D M I R E
  O   C   I   A   E
A U T H O R I T I E S
```

135

```
U N D E R S T A N D
  O   L   A   N   I
U S E F U L   C O P E
  T   T   I
F R E S H   B E A C H
  I   A   N   O
C L O T H   S T U M P
    C   E   P
O A T H   P I L L O W
  S   E   I   A   S
H E L I C O P T E R
```

136

```
I   M   P A S S
S T O N E   T E X T
  L   N   T A X I   I
A S K   G   C L A P
N   E   L O C K   I
D A Y   I   O   O D D
  L   M E N D   X   A
F L E A   E   F U N
E   Y E T I   O   G
E C H O   C A R O L
    R U B Y   D   E
```

137

```
P I C N I C   R U L E
O   O   U   M
L   D I A M O N D   P
O N E   E   E   I
  F   P T O   S   R
C O R G I   W A S T E
R   O   T H E   E
O   S   U   R A W
C   T R U M P E T   A
U   E   A   D
S A N D   N E E D L E
```

138

139

Also
available...

BRAIN
GAMES
for
clever
kids

ISBN: 978-1-78055-249-1

OVER 600 QUESTIONS

QUIZ
BOOK
for
clever
kids

ISBN: 978-1-78055-314-6

OVER 150 PUZZLES

WORD
SEARCHES
for
clever
kids

ISBN: 978-1-78055-307-8